CUTTING WATER AND EFFLUENT COSTS

CUTTING WATER AND EFFLUENT COSTS

Second Edition

John S Hills

INSTITUTION OF CHEMICAL ENGINEERS

Published by
Institution of Chemical Engineers,
Davis Building,
165–189 Railway Terrace,
Rugby, Warwickshire CV21 3HQ, UK.
IChemE is a Registered Charity

ISBN 0 85295 361 5

Printed in the United Kingdom by Galliard (Printers) Ltd, Great Yarmouth.

AUTHOR'S PREFACE

In studying the contents of this publication, it is hoped that readers will draw inspiration and profit from the practical saving techniques that are described.

The book contains chapters on the United Kingdom water industry organization and charging. These are provided as a guide and are, of necessity, general and simplified.

No special significance should be attached to the sources of the illustrations for the accounts in Chapter 3, or to the omission of other sources.

A book of this size cannot be comprehensive. The Sources of Information at the end of each chapter represent a top layer only. Many references are related to the text in the chapter, some to more than one chapter, but a number are there to lead the reader to further in-depth information, should this be required. Thus the Sources of Information sections are worth reading too!

The text contains some words which may require explanation, as follows:

- *abstraction*: any process whereby water is removed from a source of supply;
- *European Community (EC)*: the UK is part of the European Union (EU), which is primarily concerned with security and foreign policy. Within the Union, the EC covers competition and trade, including environmental law. The term EC has been used throughout the text, even though, on occasions, the correct term may be EU;
- *flocculation*: a process in which a fluffy floc is made to gather and precipitate in water in order to remove fine particles and organic matter;
- *ion*: an electrically charged atom or group of atoms dissolved in water;
- *ion exchange*: the replacement of some ions by others, for example when hard water is passed through an ion exchange resin bed enabling calcium and magnesium ions to be replaced by sodium ions to produce softened water (artificially softened water normally contains 20 milligrams per litre calcium carbonate or less — see Table 5.1 on page 82);
- *mains water*: the general supply of water provided by a water undertaker through a buried pressurized pipe distribution system serving the undertaker's customers;
- *milligram per litre (mg/l)*: a measure of concentration, essentially identical to parts per million (ppm);
- *pH*: a convenient measure of acidity or alkalinity expressed on a logarithmic scale 0 (acid) to 14 (alkaline), pH7 being considered neutral;

- *sewage*: waste water of domestic or industrial origin excluding rain or surface water;
- *sewerage*: the system of drains and pipes for the collection and conveyance of domestic and industrial waste waters;
- *trade effluent*: waste liquid, with or without suspended particles, produced by any trade or industry;
- *water undertaker*: a body authorized by a local statutory provision or Act of Parliament to supply water. The phrase has been used to describe all such bodies, both public and private, including those that carry out sewage and pollution control functions. The words *water company* and *water utility* have also been used to describe a body providing one or more of the above services. A utility which only provides mains water has been described as a *water only* or *water-supply company*. A *water service company* provides both water and sewerage services.

Once again, the author acknowledges with grateful thanks the help and advice so freely given by friends, colleagues and contacts in government departments, regulatory bodies, water undertakers, research and academic establishments, trade associations, commerce and industry, during the preparation of this and the original publication.

MINISTERIAL FOREWORD

This book is a valuable source of information for those who want to control costs arising from water usage and the treatment of waste as well as reducing the impact their business has on the environment.

There can be few sectors of industry where a reliable source of water is not essential. But in many firms, water usage is looked on as being a fixed overhead. And according to the Advisory Committee on Business and the Environment, many companies are unaware of just how much money can be saved by cutting waste. Indeed, investment in the minimization of waste can have a surprisingly short payback period.

But being good for the bottom line is not the only reason why the Government is keen to promote the minimizing of waste in industry; it is also good for the environment.

Concern for the environment brings another challenge to business — even when waste is cut to the minimum, the effluent still has to be treated. But once again, as this book shows, there is a great deal that can be done to control costs.

The United Kingdom has a great deal to offer in terms of environmental technologies, goods and services. There is available a great deal of expertise across all the environmental sectors, with particular strengths in water supply and waste water treatment, environmental monitoring equipment and consultancy. In addition the *Environmental Technology Best Practice Programme*, launched jointly by the DTI and the Department of the Environment, identifies and publicizes best management practice in this important field. I might add that larger companies also have an important role to play in helping to spread best practice among their smaller suppliers.

Richard Page.

Richard Page MP, Parliamentary Under Secretary of State for Small Firms, Industry and Energy at the Department of Trade and Industry.

CONTENTS

		PAGE
AUTHOR'S PREFACE		iii
MINISTERIAL FOREWORD		v
1.	THE NEED TO CONTROL COSTS IN INDUSTRY AND COMMERCE	1
2.	HOW THE WATER INDUSTRY WORKS	14
3.	WATER AND EFFLUENT CHARGES	37
4.	REDUCING WATER CONSUMPTION FOR DOMESTIC PURPOSES	63
5.	REDUCING WATER CONSUMPTION FOR PROCESS PURPOSES	71
6.	SAVINGS IN THE TREATMENT OF WATER AND EFFLUENT	99
7.	CONTROLLING ON-SITE WASTAGE	117
8.	COPING WITH DROUGHT AND INTERRUPTION	137
APPENDIX — USEFUL ADDRESSES		148
INDEX		153

1. THE NEED TO CONTROL COSTS IN INDUSTRY AND COMMERCE

THE ECONOMIC CASE

Keeping costs down is a necessary contribution to helping a business survive, grow and be profitable. Water-related cost saving should be part of that contribution. Small companies may well save proportionately more on their water-related expenditure than large companies. Large companies could be losing out on big monetary savings — a million pounds per year is by no means impossible!

Relatively few organizations (but now growing in number) have investigated their water and effluent charges in detail. The major exception is large water users. There is a great deal of evidence to show that valuable savings can be made by industry and commerce, paying back many times over the limited time and expenditure required to achieve them.

For the majority of businesses, charges for mains water and for effluent discharged to sewer are rising faster than inflation. As shown in Figure 1.1, charges for measured mains water have increased by 45% in real terms since March 1989. Prior to 1987, they had kept in line with inflation. Effluent charges, on the other hand, have been rising well ahead of the retail price index

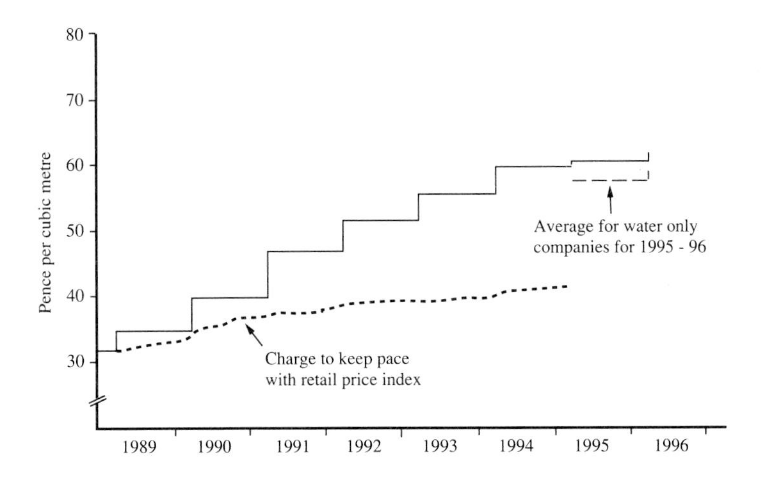

Figure 1.1 Average measured water supply charge — water and sewerage companies in England and Wales.

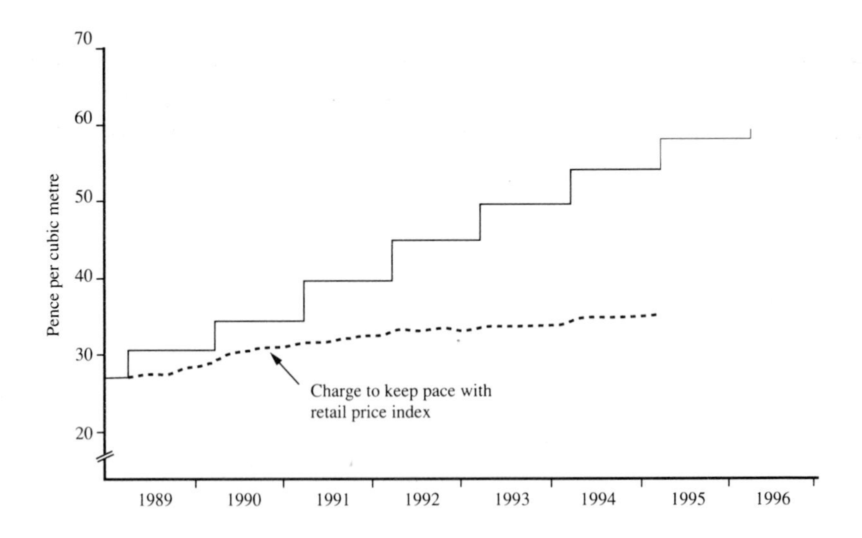

Figure 1.2 Average measured trade effluent charge — water and sewerage companies in England and Wales.

(RPI) for several years and have increased by 63% since March 1989, as charted in Figure 1.2. Water abstraction charges have been in existence in England and Wales since the 1960s. In 1991 charges were introduced for discharges to controlled waters.

THE OUTLOOK FOR WATER AND EFFLUENT CHARGES

On top of the recent increases in cost, the prospects for future increases to commerce and industry make sober reading. Prior to the 1989 privatization of the nine water authorities in England and the one in Wales, there had been an under-investment of at least £100 million per year for many years, due to government controls on public sector borrowing. Evidence of the effect of that under-investment has shown up in surveys of water quality in rivers, canals and estuaries in England and Wales.

At 1993–94 prices, the ten-year expenditure programme by the water undertakers in England and Wales to 31 March 2005 is £24,000 million. This is in order to:

- rectify the remaining backlog of work;
- improve the quality of water and effluent as demanded by European directives and, so we are told, the public.

High capital spending is already mapped out to the end of this decade. The size of the final spend will depend on who wins the tug-of-war between the European Community (EC) legislators and the Government, as influenced by the regulators, and by the public's ability to pay, voiced by bodies such as the Office of Water Services (OFWAT). Incidentally, the increase in charges for 1994–95 over the previous year (see Figures 1.1 and 1.2, pages 1 and 2) added about £150 million to the costs of UK commerce and industry taking services from the ten water and sewerage companies. As charges mount it will become more attractive for those discharging significant amounts of trade effluent to sewer to install their own pre-treatment plant in order to reduce charges. Some water companies may no longer accept complex effluents, thus adding to the pressure to build on-site treatment facilities.

Water undertakers have made considerable improvements in efficiency in recent years, thus reducing the scope for further cost reductions. The tougher financial regime has led some undertakers to charge separately for some services or activities that were previously included within individual charges.

The following recent and projected developments must also be taken into account:

- if industry takes less water, which has been the experience in recent years due to a changing or shrinking manufacturing activity, and if some large users receive discounts, then unit charges will increase as the charging base decreases;
- surprisingly, a number of commercial premises are still paying for water services based on rateable value, but a number are converting to a metered supply and showing a significant saving. The lost revenue (amounting to 18% of a recent price increase for one undertaker) has to be paid for by other customers;
- sludge disposal to sea is being phased out by 1998 in line with the EC urban waste water treatment directive. Alternative routes are very costly. Sludge disposal can represent 20% of sewerage and sewage disposal costs;
- new supplies could be more costly to exploit, on the assumption that the cheapest sources have been tapped already — leakage control and demand management may be more economical sources of additional resources;
- medical evidence and/or political pressure is requiring, and could still require, yet more costly water treatment, or supply, in order to remove certain trace elements (lead, for instance) from supplies. If the maximum concentration for lead were to be reduced from the present 50 mg to 10 mg per litre, this could cost customers in the UK £8500 million;
- increasing levels of nitrates have been and still are a problem in some raw water sources. The latest costly partners in pollution are herbicides and pesticides;
- the UK National Rivers Authority (NRA) is about to be empowered to set Statutory River Quality Objectives that will tighten the quality of many effluent discharges, thus increasing the cost of treatment;

- as the quality of a watercourse improves, an accidental pollution is likely to have a greater effect;
- EC directives will demand further significant capital expenditure. The directive relating to urban waste water treatment is now covered by UK regulations[1,2] and three others — covering bathing waters, water for human consumption and the discharge of dangerous substances to water — are awaiting revision. There are proposed directives on the ecological quality of water, energy (energy accounts for about 6% of water utility costs), landfill, hazardous waste incineration (the latter two would further limit the disposal options for sewage sludge) and a framework directive on groundwater protection and freshwater management.

These considerations all point to one conclusion. Water and effluent charges are set to continue to increase in real terms for the rest of the 1990s and into the next century. As explained later in this chapter and throughout the book, there is ample scope to cut costs in this area and improve profitability.

THE ENVIRONMENTAL CASE

Pollution has become an important issue for industry[3–6], and the increasing strength of environmental action groups[7], the partial 'greening' of the political parties and even the stock market cannot be ignored. It must be assumed that the pressure to improve certain aspects of the environment will continue[8]. It is hoped that the case for change will be based on a calm assessment of the facts and not on emotion.

The percentage of those who think that protecting the environment and fighting pollution 'is an immediate and urgent problem' has risen in the UK from 66% in 1986 to 82% in 1992, according to a recent Eurobarometer survey quoted by OFWAT. At the same time the figures across the EC have risen from 72 to 85%.

A recent *Financial Times* survey of Britain's top 500 companies showed that 30% thought environmental legislation presented opportunities, while 76% were using an environmental policy to enhance their public profile.

Decisions no longer remain solely in the hands of national governments. Much of the legislation which is needed to control water and sewage activities is in place; some of it has stood the test of time over many decades. It is assumed that most organizations will be complying with all the laws and regulations that are currently in force. It is likely that the policing of those regulations will steadily improve. In England and Wales, the NRA holds registers of analytical results for effluents discharged to watercourses and these registers are open to public inspection. Similar registers are kept by sewerage undertakers to show the performance of traders discharging to sewer[9].

SUSTAINABLE DEVELOPMENT

Disturbing environmental problems were discovered during the EC Fourth Action Programme on the Environment, including a 35% increase in water abstraction between 1970 and 1985. The EC Fifth Action Programme, entitled 'Towards Sustainability', was agreed in March 1992 for the period 1993–2000. The environment is being integrated into other Community policies. The Programme builds on the Maastricht Treaty, but is independent of it. During the Treaty negotiations in 1992, the UK succeeded in inserting as one of the Treaty's objectives a reference to the concept of sustainable growth. The UK also initiated changes to strengthen the environment chapter of the Treaty so that, 'environmental protection requirements must be integrated into the definition and implementation of other Community policies'. Thus, EC legislation relating to the environment is putting pressure on the government and regulatory bodies to achieve higher standards. These new requirements, many of which may be only marginally different from present UK practice, will nevertheless filter through to the business community. It also needs to be borne in mind that the 1972 European Communities Act required the UK courts to accept the supremacy of EC law. As a result, an individual is provided with effective remedies for the failure of the state to implement a directive properly.

The UK and other countries have been trying to relate the concept of sustainable development to their national policy-making. This concern culminated in the United Nations (UN) Conference on Environment and Development (the Earth Summit) held in Rio de Janeiro in 1992. A widely quoted definition of sustainable development is, 'development that meets the needs of the present without compromising the ability of future generations to meet their own needs'.

The Confederation of British Industry (CBI) has a Statement of Principles on Business and the Environment, in which it supports the goal of sustainable development.

In January 1994, the Government published a significant document on sustainable development, setting out the UK strategy for the next 20 years[10]. When speaking about the document on the day it was launched, the Secretary of State for the Environment made the following comments:

- 'Too long have we treated the world as conquerors';
- 'We don't hold the world as a freeholder, but on a full repairing lease';
- 'It is an offensive concept to steal from one's children';
- 'We need major changes in the way we live, not by force, but by conversion'.

The UK Government is seeking active participation by outside bodies and by individual citizens. The January 1994 document points out that the decisions, choices and behaviour of individuals in their homes and working lives are perhaps more significant than those of government and agencies in society. It also acknowledges that human beings are now the main cause of change in the world environment. The UK's population density is already one of the highest in the world. Although the UK population is not increasing rapidly, the number of households is increasing — a 14% increase is projected by 2012, with its attendant pressure on water-related services, energy and natural resources. However, this increase in water demand (under 1% overall) is expected to be met, for the time being, by a reduction in distribution losses (leakage) and falling industrial demand[11].

This is a key issue for sustainability, especially in south-east England. Although the government stresses the need to maintain essential environmental standards by regulation, its preferred mechanism is 'the more efficient economic instrument'. Does this mean even higher prices for some or all? It certainly does mean that the costs of environmental damage, or the benefits of environmental improvement, are to be built into the prices charged for goods and services. However, the document states that there will be encouragement (government assistance?) for the development of new products and processes to increase efficiency and minimize pollution and waste.

A new UN Commission on Sustainable Development has been created. It is only empowered to ask member states to report progress (not all do!).

WASTE MANAGEMENT

A 'Community Strategy on Waste Management' was presented to the EC in September 1989. The Environment Directorate General feels that the maximization of the prevention and recycling of wastes, and the minimization of final disposal, can only be achieved through the joint efforts of all those having an impact on a particular waste stream. A series of pilot projects on subjects such as chlorinated solvent waste has been launched. Producers, users, recyclers, waste managers and environment protection groups are brought together in order to look at the waste stream and develop options for action in order to minimize environmental impacts.

POPULATION

There is also the need to reflect on the likely cost and environmental effects of population growth, and on the proportion of the population that is in work, in relation to the others they support. Recent statements have included:

- the world population is said to be increasing at the rate of a quarter of a million per week, which is equal to adding more than the combined populations of Greece, Ireland, the Netherlands and the UK per year[12];
- the world population is expected to be 10 billion in 2050, 80% above its present 5.5 billion;

- the population of the world is increasing at a faster rate than the world's ability to sustain it. Apparently, as a general rule, one hectare of cultivated land will support four to five people. In the tropics, the area cultivated per person has declined from 0.28 hectares in 1971 to 0.22 hectares per person in 1986 — below, or close to, the level of sustainability[13];
- there have been calls for a 'strategy for population' which would involve a reduction in the UK population from the present 57 million to 30 million to allow a reasonable standard of living.

THE 'POLLUTER-PAYS' PRINCIPLE

The 'polluter-pays' principle[14] was publicized by the Organization for Economic Co-operation and Development (OECD) in 1975. The principle simply means that the polluter should be charged the cost of pollution control, prevention measures and remediation, as defined by the relevant public authorities. With competitive pricing for products in the market place, the likely effect of the polluter-pays principle is to cut into industry's margins, or more likely, to increase the price of the product to the customer.

Chapter 3 provides an overview of the way in which the payment is assessed for legalized discharges. However, some discharges occur outside the law. When the culprit is tracked down, the courts usually impose fines and costs. These are becoming more severe — for example, a leather producer has had to defend a court action, involving a claim of over £1 million in damages, brought by a water company after the latter tried to prove that a chemical spillage 17 years ago had caused the abandonment of a water company borehole. The leather producer won on appeal to the House of Lords, but similar defendants in the future could be less fortunate, due to the content of the House of Lords ruling[15]. A farmer was fined £5000 plus costs after pleading guilty to causing the pollution of a watercourse. A soft drinks company was fined £1000 for polluting a stream. The stream was known as the Foul Evil Brook and the pollutant was lemonade!

Case studies in a CBI booklet, *Environment Costs*[16], demonstrate that where the right action is taken, environment and safety is good for business and business is good for the environment and safety.

A radio contributor, when commenting on environmental disasters like the chemical leak in Bhopal, India, and the radioactive fall-out from the Chernobyl power station in Russia, referred to the 'ratchet effect'. By this he meant that each time society, or a part of it, reacts to an environmental issue, the ratchet will tighten by a further tooth and it will not relax. We can all feel it tightening.

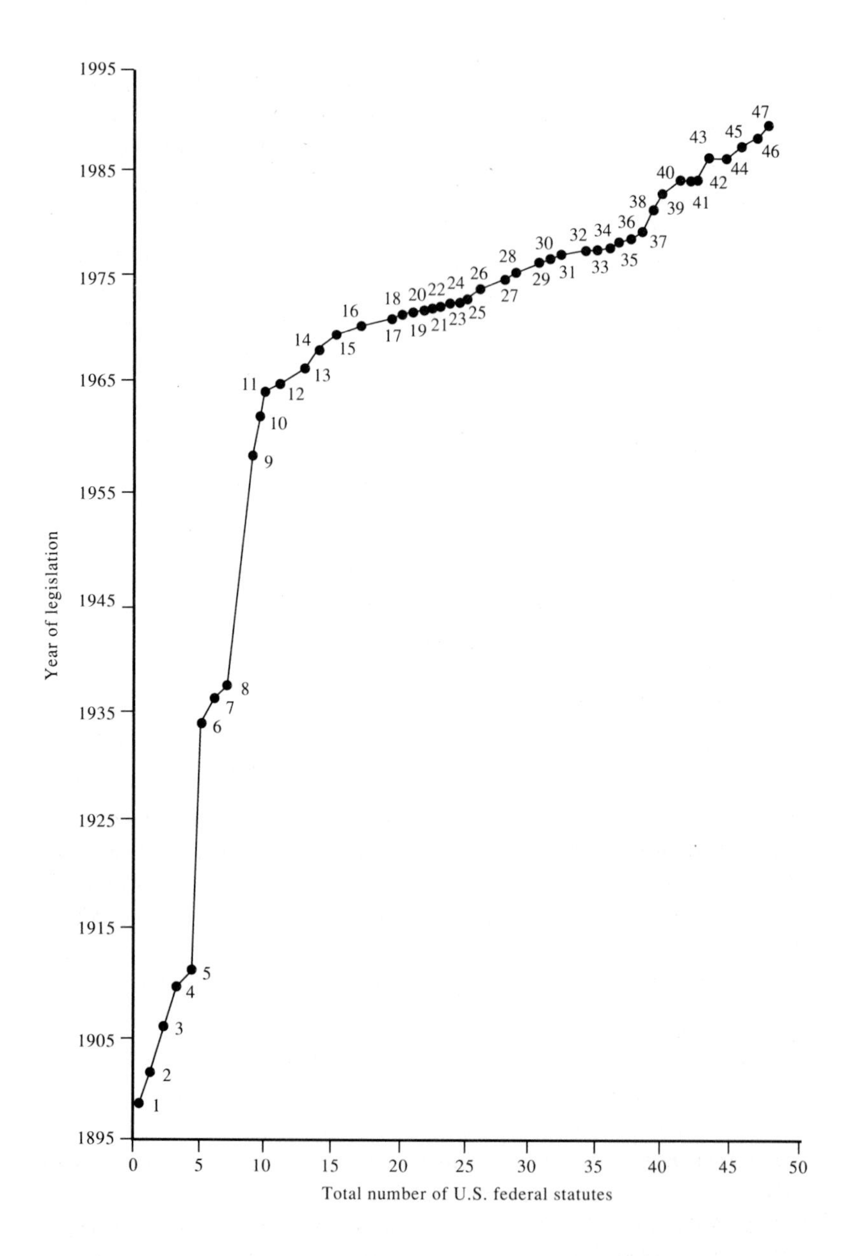

Figure 1.3 US laws on environmental protection. (Source: IChemE.)

Key to Figure 1.3:

1. Rivers and Harbors Act 1899
2. Reclamation Act 1902
3. Antiquities Act 1906
4. Insecticide Act 1910
5. Weeks Law 1911
6. Taylor Grazing Act 1934
7. Flood Control Act 1937
8. Wildlife Restoration Act 1937
9. Fish and Wildlife Coordination Act 1958
10. Solid Waste Disposal Act 1963
11. Water Resources Planning Act 1963
12. Wilderness Act 1964
13. National Historic Preservation Act 1966
14. Wild and Scenic Rivers Act 1969
15. National Environmental Policy Act 1969
16. Clean Air Act 1970
17. Occupational Safety and Health Act 1970
18. Water Pollution Control Act 1972
19. Marine Protection Research and Sanctuaries Act 1972
20. Noise Control Act 1972
21. Coastal Zone Management Act 1972
22. Federal Insecticide, Fungicide and Rodenicide Act 1972
23. Ports and Waterways Safety Act 1972
24. Marine Mammal Protection Act 1972
25. Endangered Species Act 1973
26. Deepwater Port Act 1974
27. Safe Drinking Water Act 1974
28. Energy Supply and Environmental Coordination Act 1974
29. Toxic Substances Control Act 1976
30. Federal Land Policy and Management Act 1976
31. Resource Conservation and Recovery Act 1976
32. Clean Air Act Amendments 1977
33. Clean Water Act 1977
34. Surface Mining Control and Reclamation Act 1977
35. Soil and Water Resources Conservation Act 1977
36. Endangered Species Act Amendments 1978
37. Environmental Education Act 1978
38. Comprehensive Environmental Response Compensation and Liability Act 1980
39. Nuclear Waste Policy Act 1982
40. Resource Conservation and Recovery Act Amendments 1984
41. Environmental Programs Assistance Act 1984
42. Hazardous and Solid Waste Amendments 1984
43. Superfund Amendment and Reauthorization Act 1986
44. Asbestos Hazard Emergency Response Act 1986
45. Water Quality Act 1987

46 Federal Insecticide, Fungicide and Rodenicide Amendments 1988

47. Clean Air Act Amendments 1990

THE MESSAGES FOR COMMERCE AND INDUSTRY

Motivation and explanation are the main aims of this book. In order to work on water and effluent matters, it pays to understand something about related legislation and about how water is obtained and distributed and how trade effluents and sewage are treated. Chapter 2 presents a brief picture of these subjects and the responsibility of water industry organizations in the UK. Figure 1.3 illustrates graphically the mounting pressure of laws on environmental protection in the USA[17].

Some reasons why water and effluent costs should be controlled in commerce and industry have already been given. In recent years most charges have exceeded the rate of inflation and there is continuing pressure from many environmental issues.

Although some water and effluent services may appear to be free, this could be because the costs are buried in other charges, such as rates. Most charges are abundantly clear, but with an increasingly complex charging system some require more than a superficial understanding.

Chapter 3 provides simple explanations and illustrations of most of the charges faced by commerce and industry. It also explains that there are often other charges, like standing charges, as well as the measured variety shown in Figures 1.1 and 1.2. The latter illustrations are based on averages which, although interesting, can be misleading.

Although the trend in charges, as shown in Figures 1.1 and 1.2, is important, it is what is happening in your area which is vital. Figure 1.4 shows the wide range of current charges. Since the first edition of this book (1987), besides the overall increase in all charges, the range of measured water charges of the water and sewerage companies has widened significantly. Their range of charges for trade effluent is somewhat distorted by the uniquely high charges from South West Water. The measured water charges from the 'water only' companies (27 different charges from 21 companies, due to recent amalgamations), show a distinct widening of the range. Where do your site charges fit in? If a company with a high level of water use is free to locate anywhere in England and Wales, it should bear in mind that, now and in the future, some regions have much more attractive charges than others.

Commercial and industrial sites have facilities catering for the workforce on that site. These domestic areas, the canteen and washrooms, require water supplies. The importance of water and sewage services for domestic areas can be overlooked. Chapter 4 provides valuable information and highlights the importance of a company's policy towards its domestic facilities.

Although there are roughly 11 household connections for every one in commerce and industry (the figure was 10 in 1987), about 34% of the money

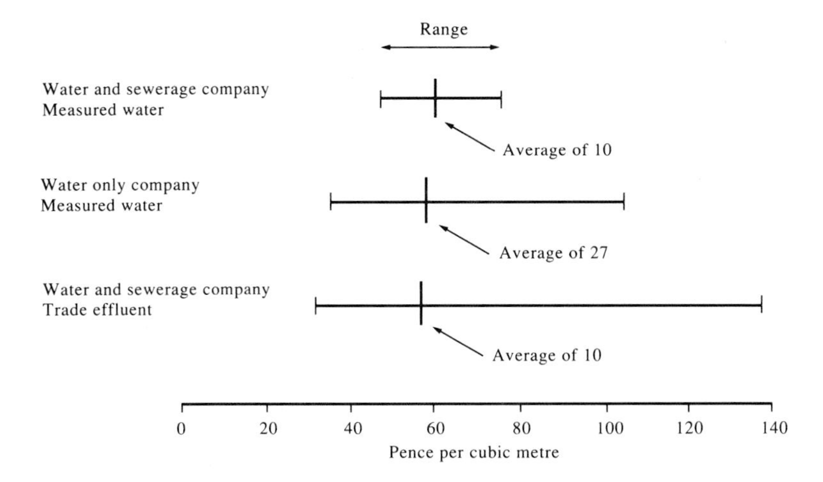

Figure 1.4(a) Spread of measured water and effluent charges 1995–96.

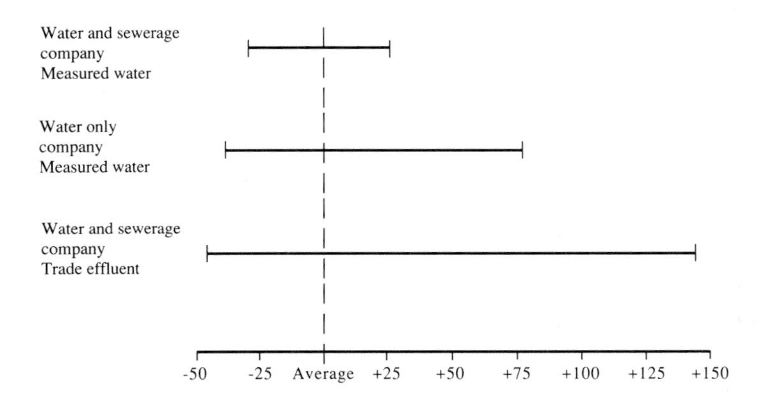

Figure 1.4(b) Percentage variation about the average for measured water and trade effluent charges 1995–96.

paid to the water undertakers comes from business customers (40% in 1987). If the water is being used inefficiently, then there must be ways of getting better value for money within the industrial processes that use the water and create the effluent. There are many water uses which are common across industry as a whole. These are highlighted in Chapter 5, together with techniques for reducing consumption and costs. Companies can learn from other people's ingenuity and be less reserved about publicizing their successes.

Although water and effluent are seen as dissimilar fluids, there are similarities in the processes that are used to treat them. Chapter 6 avoids comparing the many processes which are in use and concentrates on what can be done to make the processes more efficient in terms of energy use, chemicals and manpower. Monitoring the inputs and outputs is important in getting to grips with the treatment plant operation.

Monitoring is carried through as a theme into Chapter 7. This gives an insight into formal techniques, which exist in some industries, for surveying water use and product loss. A three-week long site survey at a food factory provided evidence that would allow significant water, product and effluent savings to be made. The survey showed that, by good housekeeping and process plant improvements, it would be possible to cut water and effluent volumes by 40% and the pollution load discharged to sewer by about 70%. The target savings for water, product, effluent and energy combined were in excess of £700,000 a year at 1995 prices.

An essential development of the technique is the creation of a daily routine for monitoring and controlling water and product losses, with the consequent reduction in trade effluent costs. Chapter 7 stresses the importance of representing water, product and effluent losses in monetary terms. This chapter is for those with determination and resolve. It is also the key to finding out what is happening to water and product in a factory. A daily knowledge of water and product loss on site can serve as a near-perfect barometer of overall plant operation and efficiency; in other words — a significant management tool.

British weather defies long-range prediction. It can swing from floods to drought and, as in early 1987, to a big freeze when, with the first return to temperatures above freezing, customers in the Thames Water area were asked to save water because one third of the water going into supply was being lost through burst pipes. The problems that come with drought and supply interruption are dealt with in Chapter 8. Extra precautions and saving techniques are listed, together with advice on preparations which can be made in advance. Global warming is likely to cause even greater extremes in weather patterns in the UK.

Knowing where to go for help, or for further information, is often more than half the battle. Sources of useful information are given after each chapter including those referenced in the text. The lists are not comprehensive, but they contain the majority of pointers which all but the very specialized enquirer will need. Useful addresses are given in a separate Appendix.

The more that is known about the water and effluent services within and outside a site, the better. 'Money down the drain' is not merely a saying; too often it is a reality.

SOURCES OF INFORMATION

REFERENCES IN CHAPTER 1

1. *The Urban Waste Water Treatment (England and Wales) Regulations 1994 (SI 1994 No 2841)* (HMSO).
2. *The Urban Waste Water Treatment (Scotland) Regulations 1994 (SI 1994 No 2842)* (HMSO).
3. *Engineers and the Environment — Code of Professional Practice*, 1993 (The Engineering Council).
4. *Manufacturing and the Environment — An Executive Guide*, 1992 (Department of Trade and Industry).
5. *Responsible Care. A programme designed to help improve the chemical industry's performance in the fields of health, safety, environment etc*, 1989 (Chemical Industries Association).
6. *Your Business and the Environment — Protecting the Environment: Next Steps for Business*, 1989 (Department of Trade and Industry).
7. *Benefiting Business and the Environment*, 1994 (Institute of Business Ethics). Research by The Green Alliance into companies that have had a financial benefit from the implementation of an environmental policy.
8. Department of the Environment, 1990, *This Common Inheritance — A Summary of the White Paper on the Environment*, plus yearly progress reports (HMSO).
9. *A Guide to Environmental Registers*. Free of charge from Denton Hall, Solicitors, 5 Chancery Lane, London EC4A 1BU.
10. *Sustainable Development — The UK Strategy. Cm 2426 1992* (HMSO).
11. *Future Levels of Demand and Supply for Water, OFWAT Occasional Paper 1*, 1994 (OFWAT).
12. Population Concern, 231 Tottenham Court Road, London W1P 9AE.
13. Hillman, J.R., 1992, Opportunities and problems in plant biotechnology — An overview, *Proc Royal Society of Edinburgh*, 99B (3/4): 173–182.
14. *The Polluter Pays Principle*, 1975 (OECD, Paris).
15. *Cambridge Water Company v Eastern Counties Leather PLC* [1994] 1 A11 ER 53.
16. *Environment Costs. The Effects on Competitiveness of the Environment, Health and Safety*, 1994 (Confederation of British Industry).
17. IChemE, 1993, *Effluent Treatment and Waste Minimisation, IChemE Symposium Series No 132* (IChemE).

FURTHER READING

Environment Industry Yearbook, annual (Macmillan Publishers Ltd).

2. HOW THE WATER INDUSTRY WORKS

The UK water industry enjoys a long and successful record of service and expertise in providing relatively densely populated islands with wholesome water and sewage purification. But because this service has been available to the vast majority of people all their lives, and because fresh and dirty water are conveyed out of sight underground, most people have only a hazy idea of how it all works.

The water cycle is one basic element which is almost entirely beyond human control and is provided free of charge. The cycle is never-ending: it rains; the rain flows into and over the land; the moisture evaporates from the land and the sea and gathers in clouds, and then the cycle is repeated. The cycle is modified to a limited extent by human activities. Vapours from cooling towers add moisture to the cycle, and chimney and car exhausts add chemicals as well. The cycle is impeded by roofs and paved areas which prevent water percolating into the ground and, in a few locations, excess water is diverted down special boreholes to underground storage, a technique known as recharge. The whole relationship is shown in a simple form in Figure 2.1.

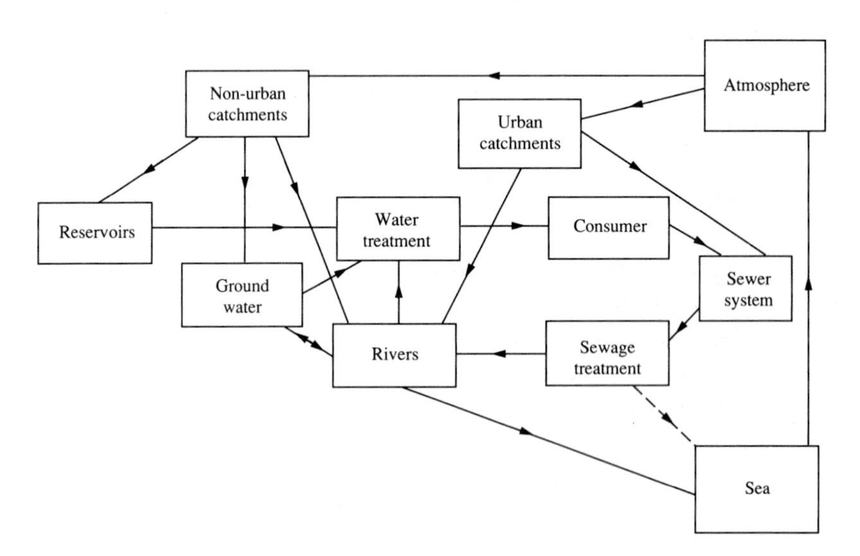

Figure 2.1 Water resources system. (Source: Institution of Public Health Engineers (now CIWEM).)

STATUTORY RESPONSIBILITIES

The responsibility for water management in the UK rests at present with ten water and sewerage companies and 21 water supply companies in England and Wales. Different arrangements exist in Scotland and in Northern Ireland.

The UK Government is responsible for water welfare and its effect on public health. This includes the negotiation of relevant EC directives and their translation into UK law. In England this task falls to the Secretary of State for the Environment, while the Secretaries of State for Northern Ireland, Scotland and Wales are responsible within their areas. There is also collaboration with the Department of Health and with the Ministry of Agriculture, Fisheries and Food on matters that are their responsibility and require their input and advice. There are also strong links between Government departments — in particular the Department of the Environment (DoE) — and the EC. A recent development in Community legislation is the concept of subsidiarity, which is concerned with the appropriate level for decision-making on matters of law and regulation — Community, national or local. Water has been included where 'existing texts should be simplified, consolidated and updated'.

The Commission intends to reorientate rules and regulations towards compliance with essential quality and health parameters, leaving Member States free to add secondary parameters if they see fit. Accordingly, Community water legislation is expected to be based on two sets of directives.

Firstly, a set of framework directives on drinking water quality; the ecological quality of surface water, quality of bathing water, and freshwater management and groundwater protection. The first and third of these would replace the existing directive on the quality of surface water for drinking and the bathing water directive. The set as a whole would replace at least parts of a number of other directives.

Secondly, the urban waste water treatment directive and the nitrates directive would remain in place as directives that 'comply with the subsidiarity principle in that they simply define an objective leaving Member States free to achieve it in their own way'.

The Commission raises the possibility of boosting the consistency of water legislation, at a later stage, through 'a genuine Community code for water'.

Present indications suggest that water-related subsidiarity may not arrive until the end of the decade. Brussels is also unlikely to be party to any significant relaxation of environmental standards.

The management of the water industry has evolved within four broad areas of responsibility:

(1) The gathering and protection of water resources, their abstraction and treatment for water supply and distribution to customers through water mains.

(2) The reception and conveyance of dirty water through sewers and subsequent treatment, before discharge to the receiving water, including the monitoring of municipal and industrial discharges and related environmental matters.
(3) Navigation, bank protection, fisheries and pollution prevention.
(4) Land drainage, including the conveying of surface water in built-up areas and flood relief and sea defence activities.

These four areas and parts of the areas are handled in different ways within the UK (see Table 2.1) and are dealt with in the sections which follow, in relation to the principal 'players' in the industry.

ENGLAND AND WALES (See Figure 2.2 on pages 18–19)

WATER UTILITIES

In some areas, mains water has been supplied for over a century by water companies. They were originally known as statutory water companies, but many have converted to public liability company (plc) or limited company (Ltd) status, and they are now referred to as water supply or water-only companies. There are now 21 of these supplying about a quarter of the mains water in England and Wales. Some customers receive separate invoices from their water supply company and from their water service company. In other areas, some customers receive a combined invoice from the water supply company if, by arrangement, the company is acting on behalf of the water service company.

There are ten water and sewerage companies, known as water service companies (WSCs), based on the areas of their predecessor water authorities. Each is owned by a water holding company which has other water and non-water interests. Some WSCs use local authorities, as agents, to maintain the sewerage and drainage system. Each WSC covers the gathering and distribution of water along with the reception and conveyance of dirty water through sewers — that is, the first two areas of responsibility listed earlier — with the exception of the monitoring of its own and other discharges to receiving waters.

NATIONAL RIVERS AUTHORITY (NRA)

The water quality in all controlled waters in England and Wales is the responsibility of the NRA, which is also responsible for navigation and land drainage, activities (3) and (4) in the list above. The NRA also conserves all water resources and redistributes and augments some of those resources.

In 1993, the NRA commenced the publication of a series of strategy documents on areas of activity including water quality, water resources, conservation and flood defence.

TABLE 2.1
Responsibilities for water-related services in the UK. (Based on CRI (CIPFA) information.)

Function	England and Wales	Scotland	Northern Ireland
Water resources			
Planning and licencing	NRA	Secretary of State Regional and island councils Central Scotland Water Development Board (CSWDB) River purification boards (licencing not applicable)	DoENI Water Executive
Development	Water supply and sewerage companies Water supply companies	Regional and island councils CSWDB	As above
Water supply	As above	As above	As above
Sewerage	Water supply and sewerage companies*	Regional and island councils	As above
Environmental protection Pollution control	NRA HMIP	Secretary of State River purification boards Island councils HMIPI	DoENI Environment Service
Flood defence and land drainage	NRA Local authorities Internal drainage boards	Regional and island councils (flood prevention of non-agricultural land) Riparian owners (land drainage)	Dept of Agriculture (NI)

Note: Detailed functions may not coincide exactly.
* The majority of district councils and metropolitan borough councils have local agency arrangements with the water supply and sewerage company in their area to undertake sewer maintenance.

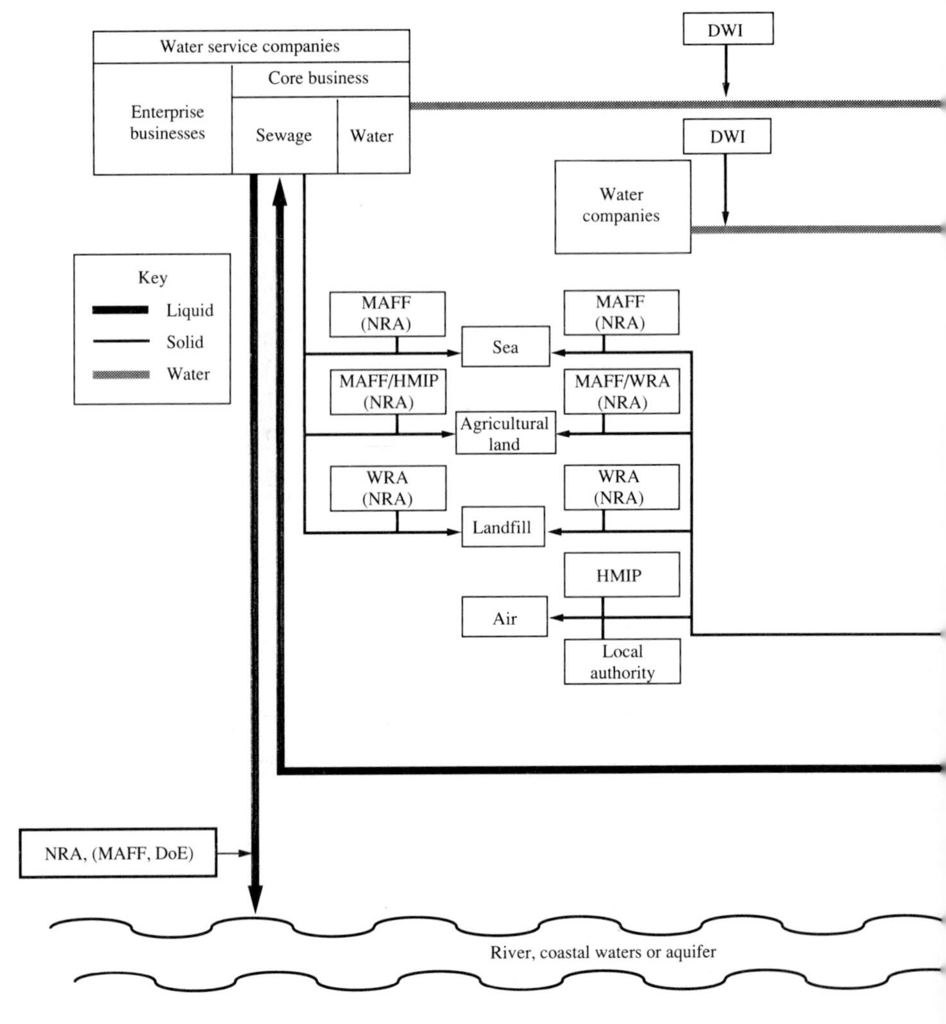

Figure 2.2 Control of water quality in England and Wales. (Source: CEST adapted from a diagram by, and updated by, John S. Hills.)

On water resources the NRA says it will review the effectiveness of licence legislation and press for amendments to laws where necessary. It will assess the reasonable needs of abstractors and revoke or reduce authorized quantities where there is no need for the original licensed quantities.

Will account be taken of the need for industry to insure, through unused licensed quantities, against the requirements of the future? This should be done as part of the assessment of need by the NRA.

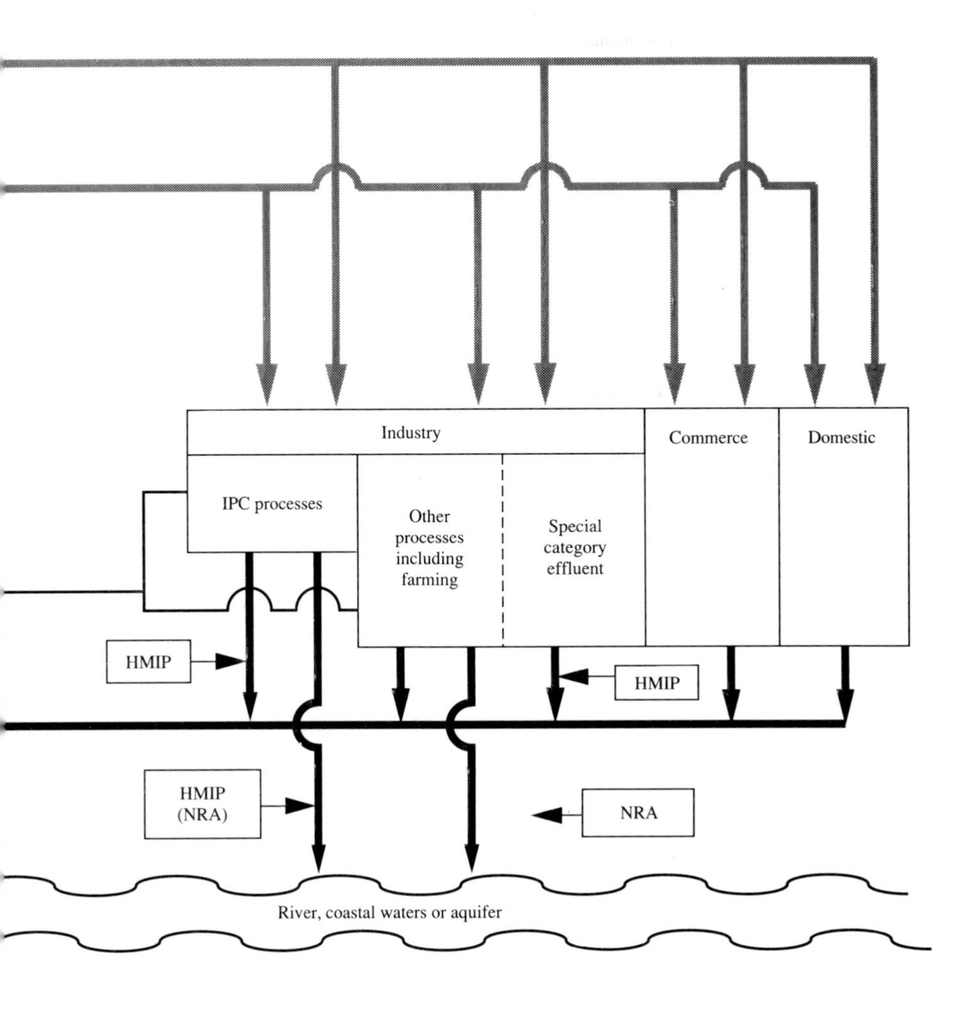

Will the NRA pay compensation when revocation occurs? It is anticipated that the NRA will try to negotiate with the abstractor, in order to avoid the situation arising, or — if appropriate — create a joint remedial scheme.

When new water resources are required, the Government wishes all parties affected to work together on the various issues involved.

On water quality, the NRA will develop a policy for the identification of Water Protection Zones (moves are already in hand to seek additional legal protection for the River Dee in North Wales) and take initiatives on monitoring and on demonstrating the benefits of minimizing water-related industrial waste at source (the latter is referred to in more detail in Chapters 5 and 7). Charging schemes will be devised to allocate costs fairly and provide incentives to reduce pollution[1].

For the purpose of setting Statutory Water Quality Objectives, regulations have been developed to implement a new system of classifying river quality in England and Wales[2].

Discharges of some complex effluents, where combinations of some substances can enhance the level of toxicity, are giving the NRA cause for concern. Based on work in the USA, the NRA is studying a protocol for the application of toxicity-based consents (TBCs). Substances such as ammonia, chlorine, metals and organophosphate pesticides are among the main culprits. Dischargers who are affected will have to seek ways of replacing the offending substance within the manufacturing process and make improvements in wastage control within the factory.

THE OFFICE OF WATER SERVICES (OFWAT)

The standard of service provided by the two types of company is driven, as before, by circumstances and, in particular, by legislation. As the companies are private monopolies, however, their financial and standard-of-service performance is overseen and monitored by OFWAT. Fundamental to the existence of each company is an Appointment (or Licence) which provides an agreed framework for the Secretaries of State and the Director General of Water Services to carry out their duties under the Water Industry Act 1991[3,4]. The Director's main duties are to:

- ensure that the functions of the companies are carried out and can be financed (including paying a reasonable return on capital);
- protect customers;
- promote efficiency and economy;
- facilitate competition.

The Director is helped by ten regional Customer Service Committees (CSCs) who, among other things:

- identify the concerns of customers;
- investigate complaints (which should first be addressed to the company providing the service);
- advise the Director General on policy matters affecting the interests of customers.

Understandably, in its early years OFWAT has had to concentrate on broad issues and on the needs of householders. Beginning in 1993, the OFWAT regional CSCs have been making special efforts to try to understand the particular problems faced by commercial and industrial customers. There is also an awareness that industry is able and needs to use water wisely.

The one OFWAT role that is seen as high profile is that of controlling the water company charges to the customer. This is done by a review mechanism which sets price limits, for ten-year periods, for the 31 water and water and sewerage companies[5]. Increases are limited by the formula RPI + K, where RPI represents inflation and K is a company-specific number (positive or negative) which limits the permitted annual increase in average charges above or below the rate of inflation. At the 1994 periodic review for the ten years from 1995/96, the K factor comprised two elements — a minus X factor covering levels of service and a plus Q factor reflecting the need for statutory improvements in drinking water and environmental quality standards.

The help of the local regional OFWAT office can be sought if a customer cannot resolve a complaint direct with the water company. In some cases, it is appropriate for complaints to be resolved by means of compensation or rebates. During the 1992 financial year, CSCs secured £75,828 in compensation and £1,147,836 in rebates from the companies. The total for the three years to March 1994 was £2.7 million.

THE DRINKING WATER INSPECTORATE (DWI)

The DWI was formed in January 1990 to check, on behalf of the Secretary of State for the Environment and the Secretary of State for Wales, that the water companies fulfil their obligations regarding the quality and sufficiency of drinking water supplies. It audits water quality information and inspects processes and procedures within water companies. It publishes an annual report giving detailed information on the water quality performance of each water company. The DWI investigates contamination and plant failure incidents that may affect, or do affect, the quality of the water put into supply. Under the Water Supply (Water Quality) Regulations 1989, the DWI maintains a list of substances, products and processes approved by the Secretary of State for use in connection with the treatment and distribution of mains water[6]. The DWI is also responsible for issuing advice on the monitoring of private water supplies[7,8]. It is expected that some of the powers of the Secretary of State will be transferred to the DWI, including the power to prosecute if water is supplied unfit for human consumption.

HER MAJESTY'S INSPECTORATE OF POLLUTION (HMIP)

Another part of the regulatory jigsaw is covered by HMIP. The Inspectorate advises the Government on pollution control practices and enforces regulations under the Alkali Act, Health and Safety at Work etc Act 1974, Water Industry

Act 1991, and Part 1 of the Environmental Protection Act 1990. The latter introduced a new system of integrated pollution control (IPC)[9] which is being applied to 200 of the most complex and polluting industrial processes.

Applications for authorization under IPC must demonstrate the use of 'best available techniques not entailing excessive cost' (BATNEEC), which is one of a complex of objectives. Under BATNEEC, a duty is placed on the operator to prevent or minimize releases of prescribed substances (see later under 'Trade Effluent', page 32), and to render harmless substances which are released. HMIP defines 'technique' as an individual pollution control technology or modification to the plant, management or output from the process. Techniques embrace the design, technology and operation (including staffing) of the process.

Where the process is likely to involve releases to more than one of the media — air, water and land — the operator must also demonstrate that the process chosen is the 'best practicable environmental option' (BPEO) for minimizing pollution of the environment as a whole. HMIP define BPEO as the option which, in the context of releases from a prescribed process, provides the most benefit or least damage to the environment as a whole, at acceptable cost, in the long term as well as the short term. (Do not try to get away with CATNAP — 'cheapest available technology narrowly avoiding prosecution'!)

In April 1993 the Government decided to create a Chemical Release Inventory, which will provide aggregated data on releases from industrial processes regulated under the IPC system. Registers, containing information on industrial plants and their operations under IPC, are available for public inspection at selected HMIP regional offices.

A memorandum of understanding exists between HMIP and the NRA on the regulation of discharges to controlled waters.

ENVIRONMENT AGENCIES

At the time of writing there is an expectation that the Government in its 1994–95 parliamentary programme will pass the necessary legislation to amalgamate HMIP, the NRA and the waste regulation functions of councils (Waste Regulation Authorities or WRAs) into a new Environment Agency. Planning for the Agency is already in hand. The new structure should be in place by April 1996.

Meanwhile the European Environment Agency (EEA)[10] has been located in Copenhagen since October 1994. An Executive Director was appointed in April 1994. The goals of the EEA will be to collect objective, reliable, comparable information on the environment, which must be technically and scientifically accurate. Its initial priorities include the setting up of a scientific committee and 'topic centres' on major issues such as waste management, air quality and water quality.

NORTHERN IRELAND

The province has clear and very direct arrangements whereby activities (1) to (3) in the list on pages 15–16 are all administered by the Department of the Environment for Northern Ireland (DoENI). Land drainage and flood protection are administered by the Department of Agriculture for Northern Ireland. Financing is by parliamentary vote. Charges are rate-based or direct to business for trade effluent and water. Plans were in hand to privatize water services but for technical reasons these have been postponed. In anticipation, however, a Water Executive was established within DoENI in October 1992 to take over responsibility for the water and sewerage functions. It is planned that the Water Executive will become an Agency in April 1996. Responsibility for the privatization process is within a separate and independent division of DoENI.

SCOTLAND

All activities listed earlier are under local government control, with the exception of river purification boards which contain equal numbers of councillors and Secretary of State appointees. Scottish regional councils are responsible for water resource development and supply, together with sewerage, sewage treatment and discretionary flood prevention. The Central Scotland Water Development Board provides bulk water resources to five councils. The monitoring and protection of freshwaters, estuary and coastal quality is in the hands of seven river purification boards. The island councils fulfil the role of river purification boards for their area of jurisdiction.

The need for water and waste water project capital throughout Scotland is assessed by the Scottish Office Environment Department and borrowing is limited by what is available in the Public Expenditure Survey, although Councils can augment their borrowing by other means. Once the allocation is made to each authority, priorities are decided within the authority.

Domestic customers connected to the public water supply are charged by way of the council water tax unless they opt for a meter. Non-domestic customers connected to the public water supply are charged either by rateable value according to the non-domestic water rate or by metered water charge. Some 98% of the population now receive a public water supply and about 97% are connected to a public sewerage system. All Council Tax payers pay a contribution to the public sewerage service, whether connected to that system or not. Non-domestic customers connected to the public sewerage system pay by rateable value according to the non-domestic sewerage rate.

Most, but not all, councils levy trade effluent charges on discharges of trade effluent to sewer. The basis for most trade effluent charging schemes is the Mogden Formula (see Chapter 3). The river purification authorities levy application, monitoring and environmental charges as well as annual charges for discharges to the water environment.

In 1993 a Government White Paper put forward proposals to create three publicly-owned water authorities. The legislation received the Royal Assent in November 1994. The water authorities will assume ownership of all the existing water and sewerage assets, maintain and add to them and take responsibility for their operation. By way of the Government's Private Finance Initiative, the new water authorities will be expected to take advantage of private sector involvement in the large programme of capital investment to comply with EC legislation.

Legislation[11] has been introduced to form a Scottish Environmental Protection Agency. Amongst its responsibilities, due to commence in April 1996, will be the promotion of cleanliness of rivers, other inland waters, Scottish tidal waters and the conservation — so far as practicable — of the water resources of Scotland.

WATER SUPPLIES

PUBLIC SUPPLIES

Public supplies are derived from two main land-based sources — surface and underground. Since 1992, sea water has been used as the source for a reverse osmosis water treatment plant installed to cope with dry weather and peak demands in the Isles of Scilly. This is unusual for the UK.

In the ten water and sewerage companies, the split between the two main sources is about two-thirds surface and one-third underground. Surface water can be of very good quality — for instance, in the Scottish Highlands catchment areas. On the other hand, river supplies in populated areas usually require treatment with chemicals, filtration and disinfection before the water is of a good enough quality to drink. Capital has been and is being invested in treatment plant and man-made reservoirs and it is expected that further investment will take place in the buried water distribution network in the second half of the 1990s.

Underground supplies are usually of good quality and normally only require disinfection before being fed into the distribution system. Some sources require iron, manganese or nitrate removal.

Measures are being taken to protect water resources from pollution. When approved by the Government, the NRA plans to introduce Statutory Water Quality Objectives for rivers. In May 1994, the Government departments issued a joint consultation document[12] on the designation of nitrate vulnerable zones (NVZs) in England and Wales under the EC nitrate directive. Farmers will be required to observe an action programme of measures, amongst other things, to help protect selected groundwater sources where nitrate levels exceed, or are predicted to exceed, the EC limit of 50 mg per litre.

Regulations[13] were made under the Water Act 1989 designating ten pilot nitrate sensitive areas (NSAs) in which farmers voluntarily agree to restrict, or change, agricultural activities. Further regulations[14] have been made under the European Communities Act 1972, in relation to the common agricultural policy of the European Community, designating an additional 22 nitrate sensitive areas. All the areas covered by NSAs also fall within the areas proposed for designation as NVZs.

PRIVATE SUPPLIES

Commercial and industrial enterprises can benefit from the existence of good surface or underground water supplies in locations where public supply is restricted, or where no public supply exists, or where it is too expensive. In England and Wales, such private water supplies are required to be licensed by the NRA. There are some exceptions — for instance, abstraction to test for the presence, quantity or quality of water (with NRA consent) in underground strata. At an early stage, it is advisable to discuss the idea for a new abstraction with the water resources section of the local NRA region and to be aware of the special procedure, involving advertisements, for making an application for a licence. In July 1993, proposals were outlined by the DoE to simplify the water abstraction licensing system. Local authority environmental health officers monitor water used for drinking and food preparation[15].

The private treatment of raw surface water can be economic or essential at particular sites (see Chapters 5 and 6). If groundwater is the likely source, then hydrogeological advice should be obtained from the NRA, a drilling contractor or a consultant. Licences for underground abstractions may be unobtainable in many parts of the country, either because there is no underground supply, or because the supply is fully allocated to existing abstractors. Due to the reduction in the UK water-using industrial base, in some parts of the country the underground reservoirs have recovered, thus allowing some fresh licences to be issued. Where a borehole can be sunk, it is not unusual to achieve a payback of the capital outlay in under two years.

A company ensures that groundwater is monitored, in a protective way, adjacent to its plant, which manufactures computer and telecommunications equipment using etching and plating processes. Wherever harmful chemicals or potentially harmful waste liquids exist on site, double containment methods are used to protect the groundwater from spillage. Regular samples are taken from boreholes, sunk on site, for analysis to provide a comprehensive picture of the hydrological health of the area[16].

SEWERAGE AND EFFLUENT TREATMENT

PUBLIC SERVICES

Public services enable domestic foul effluent and industrial and commercial discharges to be conveyed safely through sewers to strategic collection points. On reaching an inland treatment works, solids — such as rags and grit — are screened and settled out of the sewage before it is settled for a longer period to remove faeces, etc, as raw sludge. The top liquor is then biologically treated through filter beds or aerated ponds. Excess and dead bacteria are continuously removed from the process and added to the raw sludge. Thus, the treatment process yields two elements needing disposal: the treated liquid effluent and the sludge.

The treated effluent has to be of a high enough quality to allow safe discharge to a nearby watercourse. The quality of any discharge is measured in terms of the demand it makes for oxygen from the watercourse and its lack of suspended solids, and the amount of ammonia and poisonous substances, all of which are critical to the well-being of river life. Discharge quality will tighten in some areas due to the minimum standards that will be introduced by the turn of the century through the passing into UK law of the EC urban waste water treatment directive. In designated areas, secondary treatment of sewage will be required and, in sensitive areas, the removal of phosphorus and nitrogen. In less sensitive areas, primary treatment may be sufficient. The directive also requires sludge to be disposed of in an environmentally acceptable manner.

The disposal of sludge is becoming more of a problem. A significant amount is stabilized, in large air-tight containers, to make it less noxious. These containers are called digesters and the bacteria which thrive on the sludge, without oxygen, produce methane gas. The gas is used for heating on the plant or for running engines to produce electricity. About half the total sludge produced in the UK is spread on land in the locality of the works, under guidelines published by HMSO (Chapter 6, Reference 28). Some sludge goes to landfill. A quarter of the sludge produced in 1991 was dumped at sea, but the Government announced in 1990 that the sea disposal route would be phased out by 1998. The most favoured and least costly alternative is disposal to agricultural land. The more expensive process of incineration attracted 6% of sludge in 1991 and is being used increasingly, especially in areas lacking suitable agricultural outlets.

There are a number of factors which limit the rate at which sludge can be spread on land[17]. Of these, the heavy metal content (cadmium, mercury, etc) is usually of the greatest importance. As these metals are not removed by conventional effluent treatment processes, the regulator (in the case of treated effluent discharges to watercourses and of Special Category Effluent to sewer) and the receiving undertaker (for discharges to sewer) impose strict limits for specific and total heavy metals. As a result, companies with electroplating or photographic film processes, for instance, have to produce trade effluents which must meet specified low heavy metal contents before they can be discharged to sewer.

As many of the heavy metals have a value, either as scrap or for reuse in the process, the cost of adhering to these strict limits may well be fully recouped. For example, one metal recovery process developed by the Electricity Council Capenhurst Research Centre (now EA Technology Ltd — the research establishment of The Electricity Association) has found many applications[18]. A Birmingham manufacturer of domestic kettles and toasters used the recovery process in a new electroplating line, based on a two-year payback. Recycled copper, nickel and chrome solutions were worth the equivalent of £16,000 a year to the company, compared with the old electroplating line which used a chemical effluent treatment plant consuming reagents costing £21,000 a year, and which was no longer required. To the previous figures can be added the trade effluent and sludge disposal costs of £3400 a year. The new treatment produced a high quality effluent discharge with greatly reduced trade effluent charges.

The Capenhurst process was also used by a Sheffield photographic developing and printing company to recover 95% of the available silver, worth around £50,000 a year, from the spent developing solutions. The silver recovered was said to be of 99.8% purity. Thus, the processor's profitability was enhanced and the trade effluent consent limit for silver easily attained.

Historically, sewage collected from sources near the coast has been discharged, after screening, grit removal and primary treatment only, through a long pipeline into sea areas of high natural dispersion. By using the natural purification capacity of the sea, water undertakers created the most economic solution for customers. By the turn of the century, however, the urban waste water treatment directive requires that secondary treatment be introduced for discharges from specified population numbers to estuaries or coastal waters.

When an industrial discharge forms a significant proportion of the input into a local treatment works, the industrialist may be asked to make a capital contribution to the water undertaker. Under these circumstances, it is wise to look at the proposals from all angles, especially as the capital requirement could run into six or seven figures. The options are likely to be subject to an agreement that could include:

- paying for the facility over, say, 25 years at a fixed annual amount plus a trade effluent charge for the amount discharged. In this case there should be a reduction in the trade effluent charge to represent the capital element in the undertaker's costs;
- paying outright for the facility, plus a trade effluent charge abated as above;

- an arrangement to include required capacity for the future;
- private effluent treatment or pre-treatment on the industrialist's site.

One advantage of a factory being located close to a sewage treatment works could be the possibility of receiving a non-potable supply of treated effluent, should there be a suitable use for such liquid. Some UK water undertakers provide this very limited service. In Altamonte Springs, Florida, a prototype scheme is under way to install a second distribution network to convey treated effluent as a non-potable supply to all homes, offices and businesses in the community.

PRIVATE EFFLUENT TREATMENT

Although an essential extra on some sites, a private treatment plant can also be very economic on others. The cidermakers H P Bulmer won a Pollution Abatement Technology Award in 1983 for the development of an on-site pre-treatment plant to reduce highly-polluting pectin waste to a lower strength before discharge to the local water undertaker's treatment works. The plant cost about £45,000 at 1995 prices and saved more in trade effluent charges than the capital cost.

The type of treatment for industrial effluent depends on the source and composition of the waste streams. Air flotation can be used for fats and some mineral suspensions, special separators are used for oil, bacteria-supporting processes are employed for organic effluents and novel processes for inorganic wastes. These processes, alone or in combination, enable industrial effluents, including domestic sewage on commercial and industrial sites, to be either partially treated for discharge to sewer, or fully treated for discharge to a watercourse.

WATER CONSUMPTION AND DISPOSAL PATTERNS

Patterns of consumption and disposal differ throughout the UK. Figures for England and Wales show, for example, that[19]:

- over 99% of the population are connected to a public water supply;
- 94% of the population are connected to the sewerage system.

Of the water licensed to be abstracted privately or by water undertakers from inland sources in 1992 (1984 figures in brackets), excluding water power (hydroelectric)[19,20]:

- 39.7% (57%) was for public water supplies, which includes domestic, commercial and industrial customers;
- 38.9% (24.5%) was for power station use;
- 6.5% (13.5%) was for direct industrial use, which is about 40% of the total licensed quantity in 1974;
- 9.9% (4%) was for fish farming;
- 0.95 (1%) was for spray irrigation and other agricultural uses;
- 4.1% was for other uses.

One estimate of what happens to the 39.7% abstracted for public water supply suggests a breakdown as follows:

- 19% to industry for industrial use;
- 11% to commerce and service industry;
- 4% to agriculture;
- 41% to households.

The remaining 25% fails to reach the customer because it is lost through leakage from the distribution mains (length totalling 185,000 miles in England and Wales) or is otherwise unaccounted for. An increasing amount of work is being done on locating leaks and controlling leakage through pressure control and the wider introduction of meters to domestic and commercial premises. Those who are responsible for very large industrial sites could benefit from the techniques being used by the UK water undertakers[21].

Through the complete and systematic use of information technology (IT) applied to its water distribution system, East Surrey Water plc, serving a population of 320,000, has achieved a 40% reduction in burst mains frequency[22]. It has replaced hit-and-miss labour intensive leak detection methods and is, it claims, the only UK company to monitor its entire supply area through telemetry-linked district metering (an average district contains 750 properties). IT enables the creation of a self-correcting and continually improving quality loop. The principle of district metering is constant flow and pressure measurement. Minimum flow measurement (at night) allows the level of water 'unaccounted for' to be established. Thus high-leakage districts are automatically identified ensuring that manpower, used finally to locate and mend the leaks, is used efficiently. Savings in power and chemicals have amounted to £300,000 since 1986.

LEGISLATION, REGULATIONS AND CODES OF PRACTICE

Almost every aspect of water supply and effluent disposal is covered by rules of some kind. The main controls, which commercial and industrial organizations need to be aware of, are summarized.

PUBLIC WATER SUPPLIES

Public water supplies are required to be 'wholesome'. Since 1985 they have been subject to the requirements of the EC directive relating to the quality of water intended for human consumption, as translated into UK law through regulations and Government circulars[23–26]. The directive contains maximum admissible concentrations for most of the 62 parameters, minimum required concentrations for two parameters and requirements on the frequency and type of analyses. The directive also contains guide levels but, since these are not mandatory, they have not been incorporated into UK law. The Regulations are more strict in matters such as lead, pesticides and monitoring.

The standards in the UK regulations apply at the time of supply[27], that is when the water passes from the water supplier's pipe into the customer's pipe, normally at the perimeter (or curtilage) of the premises. The supplier is not responsible for the quality of the water within customers' premises, except in the special cases of the plumbing metals, lead, copper and zinc, where the water supplier is required to treat water to minimize the concentration of these metals when there is a risk of the standards being exceeded at the customer's taps. The UK regulations apply to all water used for the domestic purposes of drinking, washing and cooking and for food production purposes.

Because members of the public are employed in a business, or have access to the premises, the occupier of commercial or industrial premises needs to ensure that water used for drinking, or which will affect the wholesomeness of a foodstuff, also conforms to the requirements of the regulations. Water not used for drinking, or not likely to affect the wholesomeness of a foodstuff, does not need to meet the criteria of the directive.

In the light of new World Health Organization drinking water guidelines[28], and feedback from the operation of the directive over ten years, the EC has prepared a proposal for a replacement directive. The likely minimum time between publication of a draft proposal and the need to comply with revised parameters is eight years.

Supplies of mains water, conveyed within the curtilage of a property, are subject to the protection of Water Bye-laws[29–31]. The purpose of the bye-laws is to prevent:

- waste due to a defect, bad adjustment or bad design of a water pipe or fitting conveying mains water onto premises;
- undue consumption by knowingly using more water than is necessary for the efficient operation of water-using apparatus;
- misuse, which would be the case if water was used for a purpose which did not require water or was used when a type of use had been banned, for instance during a drought;
- contamination by changing the nature of the water as supplied, to such an extent as to be harmful or cause complaint (this is why, amongst other requirements, back-flow prevention is so important).

An organization should establish the bye-law requirements of its local water undertaker and give five days' notice in writing of alterations or new distribution pipework to be carried out within its premises. The Water Research Centre (WRc) Evaluation and Testing Centre has produced, on behalf of the water supply industry, a very useful guide to the bye-laws. WRC also tests and lists materials and fittings which conform to the bye-laws[32]. The supply of construction products, including plumbing fittings, are subject to the Construction Products Regulations 1991. Some undertakers will have terms and conditions for the supply of water, in addition to the bye-laws, in particular when the supply is taken through a meter. Clauses cover maintenance of the meter, the minimum storage required, etc. The power of the privatized water undertakers in England and Wales to make Water Bye-laws was not perpetuated by the 1989 Water Act (now consolidated in the Water Industry Act 1991), except in Scotland. The replacement for the bye-laws is presently under review, to come into force when or before the current Water Bye-laws lapse in 1997. It is advisable to keep an eye on these developments in order to become aware of the format and responsibility for this aspect of water regulation.

PRIVATE WATER SUPPLIES

Private water supplies must conform to the drinking water directive if the water is used for human consumption or is used in the food industry where its quality could affect the wholesomeness of the foodstuff in its finished form. Regulations have transposed the directive into UK law, requiring local authorities to sample and analyse private supplies[7]. The Water Industry Act 1991 gives local authorities the power to require improvements to unwholesome private water supplies.

In England and Wales, with minor exceptions, the abstraction must be covered by a licence under the Water Resources Act 1991, as mentioned earlier. The licence will specify the source, the quantities that may be abstracted and for what purpose (for example, cooling or industrial use) and the land on which the water may be used. Where water from public or private sources is supplied to others (for example, water supplied to the public or to others outside the land owned by the licence holder) the land is not specified. As part of the Government's deregulation initiative, there are moves — in areas where water is plentiful — to reduce the impact of the licensing system on small abstractors.

Water bye-laws do not apply to the distribution of private supplies, but they do preclude cross-connection between private and public water mains. It is strongly recommended that rules similar to those contained in the bye-laws are imposed by the owners of private water distribution systems.

DOMESTIC SEWAGE

Domestic sewage is conveyed away from premises through drains that are a basic feature of building construction. In England and Wales a developer will requisition the facility in accordance with Section 98 of the Water Industry Act 1991. Remote sites may require on-site facilities, such as a cesspit, which is a water-tight tank in which sewage is stored prior to regular removal by a road tanker. An alternative could be a septic tank which allows solids to settle and digest. A solids-free effluent will discharge from the tank either over land or to a watercourse. The regulator, such as the NRA, must be consulted about the acceptability of a septic tank installation and to give its consent to the discharge.

TRADE EFFLUENT

Discharges to sewer cannot be legalized until the trader has served a Trade Effluent Notice on the undertaker that will receive the effluent. The notice (under Section 119 of the Water Industry Act 1991, Part IV), is a questionnaire in which the trader gives information about himself, his business, as well as the maximum trade effluent volume, the daily rate of discharge and the likely nature and composition of the trade effluent. If the trade effluent is acceptable, the undertaker will issue a Consent to the Discharge of Trade Effluent. The Consent specifies the amount of effluent and rate of discharge, the temperature, pH and limits for polluting matter, toxic and other materials. It may also require the installation of measuring equipment and the keeping of records. The discharge may be subject to any pre-treatment conditions that could be required to meet the requirements of the EC urban waste water treatment directive (Chapter 5, References 9 and 10). It will also specify the method of payment for the treatment of the effluent.

Once the Consent is in operation, the issuing undertaker will take regular samples of the effluent for charging purposes and to check that the composition is within the limits of the Consent. The water and sewerage companies in England and Wales could change the basis for control and charging, as they strive to bring charges more into line with their costs, especially for particular types of customer.

Section 120 of the Water Industry Act covers the serving of a notice, by the trader, in respect of a discharge of any Special Category Effluent (effluent containing prescribed substances[33] — the Red List — such as the pesticides simazine and atrazine and other substances including cadmium, mercury and trichloroethylene). The undertaker will refer the notice to HMIP (acting on behalf of the Secretary of State), which may result in the imposition of conditions concerning the specified substances.

Sections 122 and 126 give the Director General of Water Services powers to determine certain appeals. OFWAT *Information Note No 21*[34] explains that the appeals procedure covers disputes about the conditions imposed and any charges which fall outside the charges scheme. The procedure does not cover appeals against any conditions imposed by HMIP governing the reception, treatment or disposal of Special Category Effluent.

TREATED EFFLUENT DISCHARGES

Discharges to inland watercourses and estuaries also require Consents from the relevant regulator. The category of discharge determines the procedures that are necessary. Any proposals need to be discussed at an early stage with the pollution control section of the relevant regulator. The subject is complex. If the proposed discharge is likely to be acceptable, a discharger in England, Wales and Scotland will be given an application form in accordance with Section 34 of the Control of Pollution Act 1974, Part II. Depending on the type or amount of discharge, the regulator decides if the application needs to be advertised. If so, the public can make representations during a six-week period and the regulator has three months after that in which to make a decision. It is important to bear in mind the time this process will take and to realize that if the regulator has not decided by the end of the three-month period, the application is deemed to be refused. As part of the deregulation initiative, the Government is proposing a streamlining of the procedures, without weakening control.

The issuing regulator takes regular samples of the consented discharge and, in England and Wales, the analytical results are placed in a register which is available for public inspection within each region. In England and Wales charges are levied for direct discharges to watercourses.

IMPLICATIONS FOR THE BUSINESS USER

Several aspects of the workings of the water industry are listed below and organizations should take them into consideration.

- It pays to discuss proposals well in advance with the water undertaker or regulator, prior to any formal notification. Experience shows that early and open discussions bring about an understanding of the issues and the best means of resolving any problems.
- Those in commerce and industry who are planning changes on a site, or a new site development, too often overlook the essential services of water and effluent. The procedure for a new project should include the need to check on these requirements at an early stage.
- A grant or financial help may be available to demonstrate a new process.
- Water undertakers, regulators and others[19,20,35–42] have published much useful information explaining their operations including, in many cases, the standards of service that customers can expect as well as complaint procedures and, in some areas, compensation.
- Commerce and industry collectively have a voice in relation to water industry issues. Trade associations and local CBI offices provide points of contact. Each water undertaker in England and Wales is allocated to an OFWAT

Customer Service Committee, on which sit individuals from varied backgrounds who meet in public on behalf of the needs of all customers.

- Steps must be taken to avoid accidental discharge of polluting matter, which can result in a fine, bad publicity, or both.
- The procedures, structure and methods of charging are evolving at a far greater pace during this decade compared with any time during recent memory. It is essential that commerce and industry constantly sift through the changes, in order to weigh the impact on their site operations and take the necessary early action.

SOURCES OF INFORMATION

REFERENCES IN CHAPTER 2

1. *NRA Customer Charter — Our Statement of Service Standards.* Free from Regional Offices.
2. *The Surface Waters (River Ecosystem) (Classification) Regulations 1994 (SI 1994 No 1057)* (HMSO).
3. *Circular 20/89 (DoE)* or *47/89 (Welsh Office)* The Water Act 1989 (HMSO).
4. *The Water Act 1989* as consolidated by the *Water Industry Act 1991* and by the *Water Resources Act 1991* (HMSO).
5. *Future Charges for Water and Sewerage Services — The Outcome of the Periodic Review*, 1994 (OFWAT). Covers price limits, infrastructure charges limits and capital spend projections, etc from 1995–96 to 2004–05.
6. *List of Substances, Products and Processes Approved under Regulation 25 and 26 for use in Connection with the Supply of Water for Drinking, Washing, Cooking or Food Production Purposes*, annual (DWI).
7. *Private Water Supplies. Circular 24/91 (DOE), 68/91 (Welsh Office)* (HMSO).
8. *The Private Water Supplies Regulations 1991 (SI 1991 No 2790)* (HMSO).
9. *Integrated Pollution Control — A Practical Guide*, 1994 (HMSO).
10. European Environment Agency, Kongens Nytorv 6, DK–1050 Copenhagen K, Denmark.
11. *Environment Agencies Bill*, 1994 (HMSO).
12. Ministry of Agriculture, Fisheries and Food, Department of the Environment and the Welsh Office, 1994, *Designation of Vulnerable Zones in England and Wales under the EC Nitrate Directive. Consultation Document* (MAFF).
13. *The Nitrate Sensitive Areas (Designation) Order 1990 (SI 1990 No 1013)* (HMSO).
14. *The Nitrate Sensitive Areas Regulations 1994 (SI 1994 No 1729)* (HMSO).
15. Department of the Environment, Welsh Office and Scottish Office, 1993, *Manual on Treatment of Private Water Supplies* (HMSO). Produced to assist local authorities in discharging their responsibilities for private water supplies.
16. *Manufacturing and the Environment — An Executive Guide*, 1992 (Department of Trade and Industry).

17. *Sludge (Use in Agriculture) Regulations 1989 (SI 1989 No 1263)* (HMSO).
18. Bettley, A., 1991, The treatment of metal-bearing liquid effluents, *Report No 2599* (EA Technology Ltd).
19. Water Services Association, annual, *Waterfacts* (WSA Publications). Concentrates on England and Wales.
20. *Using Water Wisely — A Consultation Paper*, July 1992 (Department of the Environment).
21. *UK Water Industry: Managing Leakage*, 1994 (WRc).
22. Hegarty, M., 1994, *The Strategic Role of Information Technology in Leakage Control, conference 22 March 1994* (BICS International).
23. *Circular 20/82 (DoE)* or *33/82 (Welsh Office)*, EC Directive relating to the Quality of Water Intended for Human Consumption (80/77/EEC) incorporates guidance and the text of the directive (known as the drinking water directive) (HMSO).
24. *Drinking Water Quality in Public Supplies, An Explanation of the Water Industry Act 1991 and the Water Supply (Water Quality) Regulations*, 1992 (Department of the Environment and Welsh Office).
25. *The Water Supply (Water Quality) Regulations 1989 (SI 1989 No 1147)*, as amended by the *Water Supply (Water Quality) (Amendment) Regulations 1989* and *1991* (*SI 1989 No 1384* and *SI 1991 No 1837* respectively) (HMSO).
26. *The Water Supply (Water Quality) (Scotland) Regulations 1990 (SI 1990 No 119)* (HMSO).
27. Department of the Environment and Welsh Office, 1989, *Guidance on Safeguarding the Quality of Public Water Supplies* (HMSO).
28. *Guidelines for Drinking Water Quality, Second Edition, Volume 1 Recommendations*, 1993 (World Health Organization). (Obtainable through HMSO). (*Vol 2 — Health criteria and other supporting information*, and *Vol 3 — Surveillance and control of community supplies*, yet to be published).
29. *Bye-laws and Terms and Conditions for the Supply of Services*. Available from local water undertakers.
30. *Code of Practice for Salt Regenerated Ion Exchange Water Softeners for Direct Connection to the Mains Water Supply*, 1985 revised 1987 (British Water).
31. White, S.F. and Mays, G.D., 1989, *Water Supply Bye-laws Guide* (Ellis Horwood).
32. WRc Evaluation and Testing Centre, biannual *Water Fittings and Materials Directory* (Unwin Brothers).
33. *The Trade Effluents (Prescribed Processes and Substances) Regulations 1989 (SI 1989 No 1156)* as amended by *SI 1990 No 1629* (HMSO).
34. Trade effluent appeals, *Information Note No 21*, 1993 (OFWAT).
35. *Water Services Yearbook*, annual (International Trade Publications).
36. Water Services Association, *Who's Who in the Water Industry*, annual (Turret Group).
37. *Working with business. A code for enforcement agencies,* Department of Trade and Industry Press feature. F93/49. July 1993. The Code makes enforcement bodies give companies easy access to guidance and information on regulations and related advice.

38. Customer information packs; water charges; codes of practice for customer complaints; guaranteed standards of service; market plans and annual reports are published by water undertakers.
39. *Annual Reports for DWI* and *HMIP* (HMSO).
40. *Annual Report and Accounts for NRA* (NRA).
41. *OFWAT Annual Report, OFWAT Customer Service Committee reports*. Available from regional offices.
42. Scottish Office Environment Department annual publication on the quality of drinking water in Scotland.

FURTHER READING

Brassington, R., 1995, *Finding Water — A Guide to the Construction and Maintenance of Private Water Supplies*, second edition (John Wiley and Sons).

Council Directive 93/76/EEC of 13 September 1993 to limit carbon dioxide emissions by improving energy efficiency (HMSO). Includes programmes for the billing of heating and hot water costs on the basis of actual consumption.

Control of Pollution Act 1974 (HMSO).

Construction Products Regulations 1991 (SI No 1620) (HMSO).

Proposal for a Council Directive on integrated pollution prevention and control. COM (93) 423 final (HMSO). The aim is to provide measures and procedures to prevent, wherever practicable, or to minimize emissions from industrial installations so as to achieve a high level of protection for the environment as a whole. The IPPC concept is embraced in the UK IPC system.

Environmental Law Monthly (Monitor Press).

Environment Newsletter (Confederation of British Industry).

The Environmental Protection Act 1990 (HMSO).

The Environmental Protection (Prescribed Processes and Substances) Regulations 1991 (SI 1991 No 472) as amended (HMSO).

Price, M., *Introducing Ground Wat*er (Allen and Unwin).

An Introduction to Drinking Water Quality, 1993 (Chartered Institution of Water and Environmental Management).

Public Health Acts 1936, 1937 and *1961* (HMSO).

Water Bulletin (WSA Publications).

Water and Environment Management (Thomas Telford).

Water and Waste Treatment (Faversham House Group).

Water Services (International Trade Publications).

The Water (Scotland) Act 1980 (HMSO).

World Water (Faversham House Group).

3. WATER AND EFFLUENT CHARGES

Although there are common elements in most charging schemes in the UK, there is no single method of charging throughout, with the exception of the unifying approach by HMIP and the NRA in England and Wales.

For decades, the Confederation of British Industry (CBI) has had no difficulty in saying that its members (from commerce and industry) are willing to pay for work done. In other words, the cost of providing water and effluent services should be divided fairly among those who buy those services. And if there is a need to control the important aspects of water and effluent quality and services, this should be done by regulation. But recently two words, 'incentive charging' have crept into pronouncements by the Secretary of State for the Environment and his Department. It will be interesting to see if and how incentive charging will be applied, and what the reaction will be from the customers (see under 'National Rivers Authority', page 41).

In Scotland, water supply services are charged to domestic customers by the local government regions through a council water tax or, if requested, a measured charge and, for non-domestic water use, by rateable value based on non-domestic water rates or by measured charges. Only seven of the twelve regional and islands councils levy trade effluent charges and there is a non-domestic sewerage rate for used water from non-domestic business. Sewerage services for domestic customers are paid for in the general council tax.

In Northern Ireland, only a proportion of the services provided are charged directly to the customer. There are no charges for domestic quality used water from any property, the cost being included in the regional rate. Only commerce, industry, agriculture and public bodies pay directly for mains water and large dischargers of trade effluent pay for treatment, if given. The rest of the costs are recovered by rates or a property tax.

In England (with nine water and sewerage companies and 20 water only companies), and in Wales (with one water and sewerage company and one water only company), water undertakers raise an almost complete set of charges (they are not allowed to charge for highway drainage) which are not subsidized by local or central government. As a result, at least one water and sewerage company has over ten types of invoice.

A brief explanation of the main payments made by commerce and industry is set out in this chapter using illustrations from England and Wales.

Comprehensive information is contained in surveys of United Kingdom water industry charges and costs[1,2].

COST STRUCTURE OF THE WATER SUPPLY INDUSTRY

As customers in England and Wales are expected to pay all the costs of water and effluent services, it is useful to know how the costs arise. Charges are levied by the water undertakers, by the regions of the NRA and by HMIP.

WATER UNDERTAKERS

Water and sewerage company combined capital and operating cost expenditure is shown in Figure 3.1. Note the present capital intensive nature of the business.

The Appointment licence requires water undertakers in England and Wales and the Director General of OFWAT to ensure that the charges do not discriminate unduly against, or show undue preference to, any class of customers or potential customers. It follows that the costs depicted in Figure 3.1 have to be allocated fairly when invoiced to the customer. Table 3.1 shows which services attract a separate direct charge at present throughout the UK; it also includes direct charges from regulators.

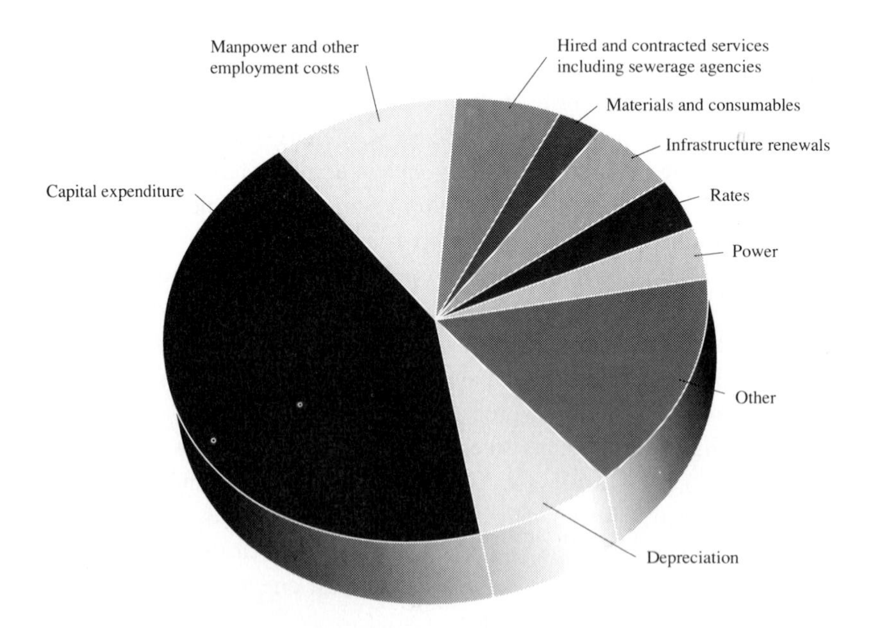

Figure 3.1 Water and sewerage company 1993–94 operating costs and capital expenditure. (Source: Water and sewerage company accounts and *Waterfacts '94*.)

TABLE 3.1
Summary of services directly charged to customers. (Based on CIPFA and CRI information.)

	Northern Ireland		Scotland		England and Wales	
	House-holds	Other users	House-holds	Other users	House-holds	Other users
WATER RESOURCES AND SUPPLY						
• Water resources	No	No	No	No	Yes[1]	Yes
• Piped supply	No	Yes	Yes	Yes	Yes[2]	Yes[2]
DRAINAGE						
• Rainwater from property via sewer	No	No	No	No	Yes	Yes
• Land drainage via river	No	No	No	No	No	Yes[3]
USED WATER AND ENVIRONMENT						
• Used water from people via sewer	No	No	No	Yes	Yes	Yes
• Used water from manufacturing via sewer	N/A	Yes	N/A	Yes[4]	N/A	Yes
• Discharge direct to river, coast, lake or underground	No	No	No	Yes	No[5]	Yes
• Environmental monitoring and protection	No	No	No	No	No	No

Notes:
[1]: Only made when several households join to form a company.
[2]: Includes element for abstraction charges (water resources) paid by water supply company.
[3]: Charged by internal land drainage districts, where they exist, and by NRA Anglian Region.
[4]: Not fully implemented.
[5]: Annual charges raised for discharges exceeding 5 m^3 per day.
N/A = not applicable.

It is not always realized that a high proportion of the costs within a water undertaker arise from the provision of the capacity to serve peak flows for water supply and surface, foul and industrial drainage. A proportion of the costs of these fixed assets has appeared in standing charges. However, OFWAT has been encouraging water undertakers to reduce standing charges and to re-allocate the costs to the volumetric charges.

The Water Industry Act 1991 also allows charges schemes to 'make different provision for different cases' and for individual agreements 'with any person in any particular case'. There is mounting pressure from large water users to obtain special rates of charge. An example is an airport which is served off a large trunk distribution main. In this case, the water company does not have the cost of maintaining the smaller distribution pipes which serve the overwhelming majority of customers. In 1993–94 North West Water and East Surrey Water introduced tariffs for a class of large industrial customers. Commencing in 1994–95 Anglian, Severn Trent and Essex and Suffolk introduced cost-based tariffs for particular classes of customers. It is therefore probable that business discount tariffs (the description used by some, despite the cost-based nature of the tariffs) will spread more widely in England and Wales (at April 1995 18 companies had introduced separate tariffs for large users). If choosing a new site for a business likely to use significant quantities of water, it could be important to ensure that it is alongside a trunk main. Inevitably, small businesses will see discounts to large businesses as a potential price increase for small businesses.

Table 3.2 illustrates a banding system for discounts. Following extensive investigations by Bristol Water, it was established that economies of scale brought cost reductions for consumptions above 50 megalitres per year. The system is related to a standard measured tariff and, by incorporating increasingly

TABLE 3.2
Banded business discount tariff — mains water. (Source: Bristol Water.)

Band	Eligible range, Ml per year	Standing charge, £	Volume discount, %
A	>500	24,141	25
B	250–500	11,091	20
C	100–250	4566	15
D	50–100	3000	12

higher standing charges for each band, it creates ever higher break-even points thus dissuading customers from wasting water.

Large users of water (those using, or expecting to use, more than 250 Ml a year) can 'shop around' to try to obtain a cheaper supply from a company other than their existing supplier. These arrangements, called 'inset appointments', can only be made by the OFWAT Director General following an application and public consultation. At the time of writing, such an arrangement has still to emerge, although applications have been made to OFWAT.

Another aspect of competition which has been suggested, is the 'common carrier' concept. This is already in use in the electricity and telephone distribution system and, for water, would involve a customer receiving water from an external supplier utilizing the distribution pipework of the local water company. However, there are a number of obstacles to be overcome, such as the responsibility for water quality. This is another case where it is important to keep in touch with continuing developments in the water industry.

NATIONAL RIVERS AUTHORITY (NRA)

The NRA levies charges for all licensable abstractions from designated sources of raw water supply. They also charge for consented direct discharges to controlled waters which include river, coast, lake or underground. A charge is made for making application for such abstractions and discharges. See Table 3.3 for a simplified general summary of the application of capacity and usage charges.

The NRA 1993 *Water Resources Strategy document*[3] held out the prospect of introducing incentive charging schemes. It said this could have a marked impact upon the NRA's 'role in authorizing future abstractions, alter the way in which existing licences are allocated and also produce opportunities for the way in which surplus funds are deployed'. The assumption is that some abstractors are going to pay more in order to provide a real incentive to change attitudes and behaviour. However, introducing incentive charging will need a change in legislation. Licence-holders need to keep closely in touch with developments.

Another financial aspect of the NRA's role is to take court action, when appropriate, against those who contravene pollution laws, those who are in contravention of an abstraction licence and unlicensed abstractors. The cases usually receive publicity — which is not good for the image of the offender! Examples include a £48,800 fine for the illegal discharge to a watercourse of three million gallons of pig effluent from a Suffolk farm. A Midlands firm was fined £3000 for allowing the spillage of fuel oil into a stream. Fines are paid into Court and do not benefit the NRA financially. If costs are awarded, they are paid to the NRA.

TABLE 3.3
Application of capacity and usage charges. (Based on a CIPFA illustration.)

Service	Charge made for	Basis and unit of charge
Water resources	Capacity made available and licensed	Pro rata to maximum authorized abstraction, multiplied by factors related to impact on water resources
	Discharges to controlled waters	Pro rata to maximum consented discharge, multiplied by factors related to impact on receiving water
Piped supply	Metering capacity Capacity available for use	Per meter per charge period according to size: (i) per connection, scaled according to diameter, or (ii) per unit of property valuation
	Usage	(i) according to meter readings, or (ii) per unit of property valuation, taken with capacity charge
Surface water	Capacity connected to sewer	(i) per unit of surface area connected, or (ii) per unit of property valuation, or (iii) per property connected, or (iv) per water supply connection (scaled by size)
	Capacity of river drainage	(i) directly on each unit of property valuation and agricultural land area, or (ii) indirectly through increase in council tax or local rates on property except agricultural land
Used water	Capacity	(i) per unit of property valuation, or (ii) per water supply connection (scaled by size), or (iii) per property
	Use by people	(i) per unit of property valuation, or (ii) according to supply meter readings less loss in use allowances
	Use in process of manufacture	Per unit of volume, plus per unit of strength requiring treatment

Note: see Table 3.1 (page 39) and text for information on who levies charge — for example, regulator, internal land drainage district or undertaking.

HER MAJESTY'S INSPECTORATE OF POLLUTION (HMIP)
Charging began in April 1991 for integrated pollution control (IPC) and Radioactive Substances Act 1993 regulation. Fees and charges are based on the amount of regulatory effort involved in carrying out the assessment of applications and other regulatory functions, measured in terms of man days.

There is an application fee (£3860 for 1995/6) for each process, or component process, within a large installation covered by the IPC legislation. A variation fee is charged (£1290 per component for 1995/6) to cover the authorization costs when a process has been altered. An annual subsistence charge is levied to cover the costs of the continuing oversight and monitoring of the authorized process by HMIP (set at £1805 per component for 1995/6) plus, in a limited number of cases, a direct charge for check monitoring.

METHODS OF CHARGING

The way in which water undertaker costs are dealt with, or recovered, has been simplified into three categories that are outlined here.

INITIAL COSTS
In this case, developers and customers are required to provide, at their own expense, the original mains water or drainage installation to meet either building or water undertaker regulations. The pipework outside the curtilage, assuming it is up to standard, is then adopted by the undertaker. There are connection and infrastructure charges and arrangements to guarantee income. The local water undertaker will give information on requirements for new developments and connections. The infrastructure charges in England and Wales had been thought by some to be too high. OFWAT has agreed with the water companies* that, from April 1995, a basic charge of £200 applies to each new connection to a water main and to a connection to a public sewer. The charge will be adjusted annually in line with inflation.

CAPACITY CHARGES
These are used either as a total charge, based on the size of a connection or the size of the property, or to form part of a metered charge. In England and Wales

---

* At the time of writing, the situation regarding Portsmouth Water Plc and South West Water awaits the outcome of the referrals to the Monopolies and Mergers Commission, following the result of the OFWAT Periodic Review in 1994.

they have been changed, under guidance from OFWAT, into what are best described as annual standing charges.

USAGE CHARGES

For non-domestic customers, charges are most often based on meter readings which relate to mains water. From these readings, foul and trade effluent can be charged in addition to any capacity charge payable. Trade effluent is more often separately measured as the basis for the charge. Some undertakers offer an assessed charge based on the (usually small) number of employees located at the premises.

A simplified summary of how capacity and usage are charged in the UK is shown in Table 3.3 on page 42. The table also includes services provided by internal land drainage districts and the regulators.

CHARGES FOR THE PRINCIPAL SERVICES

Water and sewerage companies, water supply companies and the NRA recover their costs by charging for the main services and facilities shown in Figure 3.2. The size of each segment in the chart also reflects the costs to the companies for providing that service. The water supply companies provide about a quarter of the total piped water supply.

It is important for any organization to ensure that the charges it pays correspond accurately to the services it is receiving. Significant savings can be achieved by checking invoices. If staff are not available to carry out this task, then a commercial organization, which specializes in analysing invoices for water, effluent and other services could be used, checking whether a client is being overcharged and whether tariffs are correct for each location. Payment is usually by a service charge, based on the total site expenditure for the service being monitored, plus a percentage of the refunds and credits obtained on a client's behalf. Water bills need extra scrutiny when meters are changed and especially when the units of measurement change — for example, from imperial to metric.

One company providing such a service obtained water bill refunds amounting to £75,000 for a Welsh pharmaceutical firm and £20,000 for a local authority in the South of England. Total savings obtained for clients are said to be running at over £1 million a year.

A school moved out of two old buildings that were sold but water bills continued to arrive at the county council and were paid. By the time the error was discovered, the new owners of the buildings had benefited from the non-payment of some £6000.

The staff of OFWAT CSCs can be instrumental in helping to rectify charging errors which cannot be resolved by contact between the customer and the water undertaker. Of the rebates negotiated by the ten CSCs in 1993/94, 73% was on behalf of non-domestic customers.

The facilities at each site determine the way in which charges are combined or levied. Tables 3.4 and 3.5 (see pages 46 and 47) illustrate how charges are applied in one water and sewerage company area. The grid is a useful method of illustrating and understanding charging schemes. The actual charging structure differs from one undertaker to another.

For ease of identification, the services shown in Figure 3.2 have been allocated a reference letter. These letters are used to highlight the position of each charge in the specimen accounts, excepting land drainage, shown in Figures 3.3 to 3.6. From July 1990, industrial water supply and the emptying of cesspools and septic tanks have been subject to the addition of value added tax (VAT).

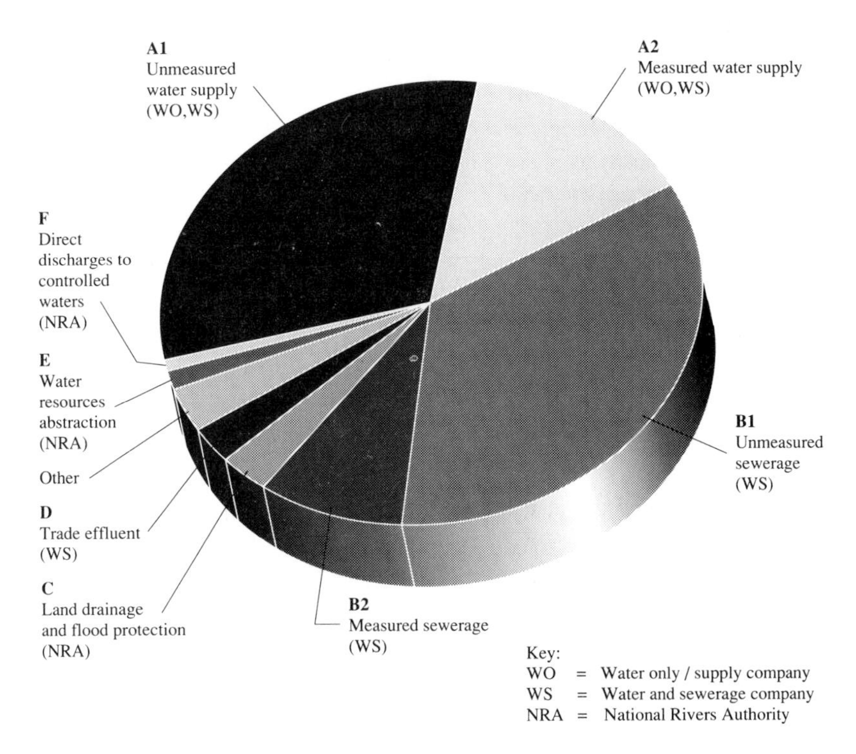

Figure 3.2 Water supply company, water and sewerage company and NRA 1993–94 income — England and Wales. (Source: OFWAT, NRA, *Waterfacts '94*.)

TABLE 3.4
Unmeasured tariffs. (Source: Severn Trent Water.)

Service details	Unmeasured water supply, pence / £ rateable value (RV)	Full unmeasured sewerage, pence / £ rateable value	Surface water drainage, pence / £ rateable value	Used water and surface water drainage (lower rate), pence / £ rateable value
Connected for water supply, all sewage drains to public sewer	✔	✔		
Connected for water supply, all sewage drains to cesspool or septic tank (no connection to public sewer)	✔			
Connected for water supply, surface water drains from property to soakaway and foul sewage drains to public sewer	✔			✔
No connection for water supply, surface water drains from property to public sewer			✔	

✔ indicates tariffs applicable

STEPS TO MINIMIZE WATER AND EFFLUENT DISPOSAL CHARGES

Set out next are some points to consider and steps to take for minimizing water and sewerage charges.

UNMEASURED WATER SUPPLY (A1)

Figure 3.3 on page 48 shows an account where charges for supply are based on rateable value. The present law requires that this base be phased out by 31 March 2000, but the Government has announced that legislation will be introduced to allow unmeasured charges to be derived from rateable values after that date.

TABLE 3.5
Measured tariffs. (Source: Severn Trent Water.)

Service details	Measured water supply*, pence/m^3	Measured used water, pence/m^3	Surface water drainage**, pence/£RV	Surface water drainage (lower rate)**, pence/£RV	Surface area measurement, £/100m^2
Connected for water supply, all sewage drains to public sewer (where the customer has not opted for surface area measurement)	✔	✔	✔		
Connected for water supply, all sewage drains to cesspool or septic tank (no connection to public sewer)	✔				
Connected for water supply, used water drains to public sewer and surface water drains to soakaway	✔	✔		✔	
Connected for water supply, all sewage drains to public sewer and the customer had opted for measurement of surface area drained (existing non-domestic premises only)	✔	✔		✔	✔
No connection for water, surface water drains to public sewer and customer had opted for surface area measurement (existing non-domestic premises only)				✔	✔

✔ indicates tariffs applicable

* For the purpose of identifying liability for sewerage charges, the metering of water supply from an abstracted water source (well or borehole) may be substituted in the measured water supply column.

** For properties without a 1989/90 rateable value then a fixed charge applies instead of pence per £RV.

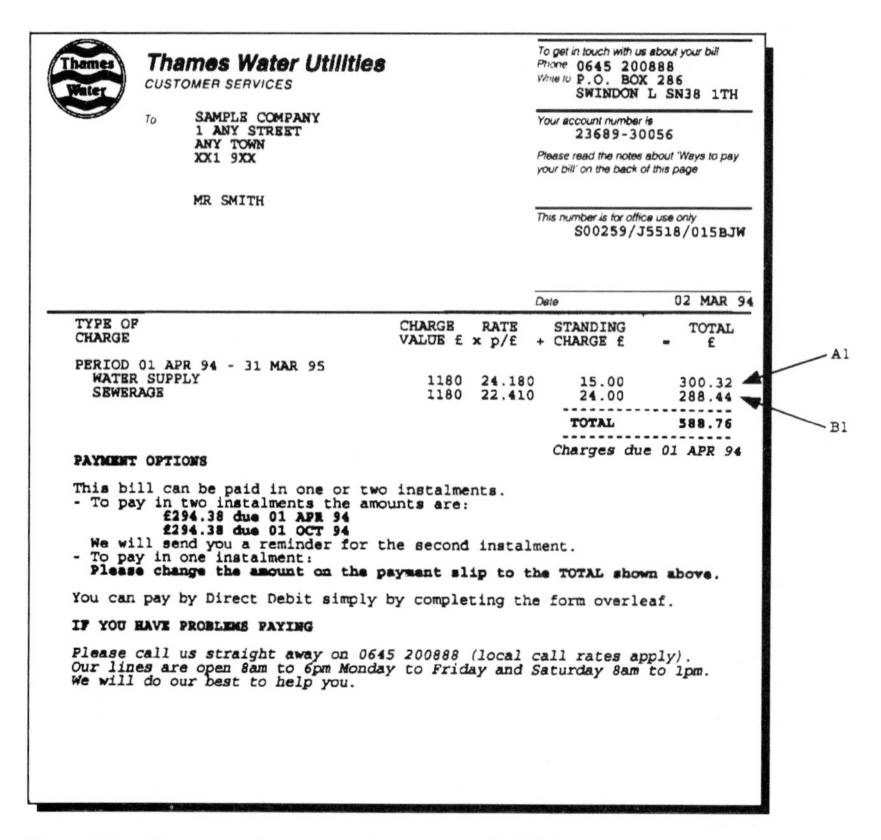

Thames Water
Thames Water Utilities
CUSTOMER SERVICES

To get in touch with us about your bill
Phone 0645 200888
Write to P.O. BOX 286
SWINDON L SN38 1TH

To SAMPLE COMPANY
1 ANY STREET
ANY TOWN
XX1 9XX

MR SMITH

Your account number is
23689-30056

Please read the notes about 'Ways to pay your bill' on the back of this page

This number is for office use only
S00259/J5518/015BJW

Date 02 MAR 94

TYPE OF CHARGE	CHARGE VALUE £	x RATE p/£	+ STANDING CHARGE £	= TOTAL £
PERIOD 01 APR 94 - 31 MAR 95				
WATER SUPPLY	1180	24.180	15.00	300.32
SEWERAGE	1180	22.410	24.00	288.44
			TOTAL	**588.76**

A1
B1

Charges due 01 APR 94

PAYMENT OPTIONS

This bill can be paid in one or two instalments.
- To pay in two instalments the amounts are:
  £294.38 due 01 APR 94
  £294.38 due 01 OCT 94
  We will send you a reminder for the second instalment.
- To pay in one instalment:
  Please change the amount on the payment slip to the TOTAL shown above.

You can pay by Direct Debit simply by completing the form overleaf.

IF YOU HAVE PROBLEMS PAYING

Please call us straight away on 0645 200888 (local call rates apply). Our lines are open 8am to 6pm Monday to Friday and Saturday 8am to 1pm. We will do our best to help you.

Figure 3.3 Unmeasured water services account (A1, B1).

It may well be cheaper to change to a metered supply. In 1993/4 there were still 440,000 non-household properties in England and Wales which were not metered. Many relatively highly-rated commercial premises have still not taken up the metering option and are paying more than necessary. An illustration of the large amount of excess funds that have ceased flowing from commerce and industry to one undertaker is that 1% of the 6.6% rise in charges for 1994–95 was due to the need to compensate for those changing from a rate-based charge to a meter (that is, 18% of the total increase!). Another alternative for a small firm in commercial premises is to take up an assessment option, if available from the undertaker, where the charge is based on the facilities and number of employees.

Finally, if payment is based on a connection size, it could be economic to reduce that size, provided that the reduction will not limit present or medium-term activities.

MEASURED WATER SUPPLY (A2)

Figure 3.4 is an example of a metered water services account. How these prices have changed is shown in Figure 1.1 (see page 1) and their current ranges in Figure 1.4 (see page 11). The fact that the supply is measured allows the customer to take regular readings in order to help control water usage and costs. Checks should be made for leakage on the customer's side of the meter — it is the customer who pays for wasted water. Plotting weekly readings graphically allowed a leak to be detected five weeks after the installation of a meter at a West Country laboratory.

If there is an associated annual charge based on meter size, as in Figure 3.4, the meter may be oversized for the maximum rate at which the water is taken. Has a storage tank been installed which can now be filled over a longer period through a smaller meter? If the premises are served by more than one connection, can the number be reduced, thereby cutting out standing charges?

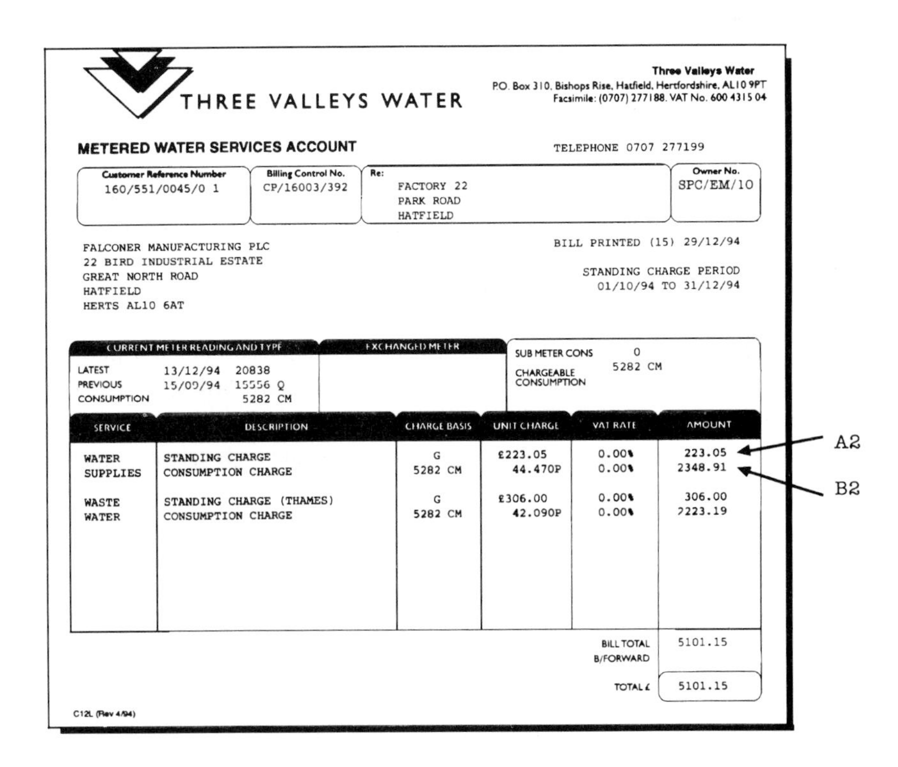

THREE VALLEYS WATER

Three Valleys Water
P.O. Box 310, Bishops Rise, Hatfield, Hertfordshire, AL10 9PT
Facsimile: (0707) 277188. VAT No. 600 4315 04

METERED WATER SERVICES ACCOUNT

TELEPHONE 0707 277199

Customer Reference Number	Billing Control No.	Re:	Owner No.
160/551/0045/0 1	CP/16003/392	FACTORY 22 PARK ROAD HATFIELD	SPC/EM/10

FALCONER MANUFACTURING PLC
22 BIRD INDUSTRIAL ESTATE
GREAT NORTH ROAD
HATFIELD
HERTS AL10 6AT

BILL PRINTED (15) 29/12/94

STANDING CHARGE PERIOD
01/10/94 TO 31/12/94

CURRENT METER READING AND TYPE			EXCHANGED METER	
LATEST	13/12/94	20838		SUB METER CONS 0
PREVIOUS	15/09/94	15556 Q		CHARGEABLE CONSUMPTION 5282 CM
CONSUMPTION		5282 CM		

SERVICE	DESCRIPTION	CHARGE BASIS	UNIT CHARGE	VAT RATE	AMOUNT
WATER SUPPLIES	STANDING CHARGE	G	£223.05	0.00%	223.05
	CONSUMPTION CHARGE	5282 CM	44.470P	0.00%	2348.91
WASTE WATER	STANDING CHARGE (THAMES)	G	£306.00	0.00%	306.00
	CONSUMPTION CHARGE	5282 CM	42.090P	0.00%	2223.19

BILL TOTAL 5101.15
B/FORWARD
TOTAL £ 5101.15

C12L (Rev 4/94)

Figure 3.4 Metered water services account (A2, B2).

Be sure, when rearranging the pipework for a single feed, that no dead-legs remain as they represent a quality risk. For those in England and Wales, it should be noted that OFWAT is putting pressure on regulated undertakers to reduce the size of the standing charges, recouping the loss on the charge per cubic metre. This may be financially advantageous for those taking quantities at or below the break-even point, but not so for sites with a high water usage.

UNMEASURED SEWERAGE (B1)

In Figure 3.3 (see page 48) a charge for used domestic water is also being raised on the basis of rates. The comments in 'Unmeasured Water Supply (A1)' (page 48) also apply here. (See also 'Rain and Surface Water', page 52). Remember that no connection to the sewer means no charge.

MEASURED SEWERAGE (B2)

The account shown in Figure 3.4 also contains charges for used domestic water on a metered basis. The comments in 'Measured Water Supply (A2)' (page 49) also apply here. In addition, the effect of any water supply meter reading errors against the customer are doubled if sewerage is paid for on the basis of measured water intake. If intake is the only measure, does all the water go down the sewer? Some may evaporate, or be used in a product which leaves the factory, or be discharged to a watercourse or a soakaway. If this represents at least 10% of the intake, the amounts should be agreed with the water undertaker so that the charge can be reduced accordingly. The NRA charges for a discharge to a watercourse or soakaway (see 'Direct Discharge to Rivers, etc' page 61 etc).

RAIN AND SURFACE WATER

The entry of surface water (and any groundwater) into the public sewers, and its conveyance, treatment and disposal, are usually an integral part of the sewerage charge. However, if no such water gains access to the sewer from the site, because positive alternative arrangements have been made, it is possible to have the charges reduced by the proportion attributable to the undertaker's surface water costs.

LAND DRAINAGE AND FLOOD PROTECTION (C)

For each land drainage district in its region, the local NRA office charges English and Welsh county councils (and internal drainage boards where they exist) for the costs incurred. This charge, called a levy, is then transferred by the county to district councils. The district councils then pass on the charge as an element of the council tax on all premises in their area. The tax does not reflect the full cost of capital schemes, as a variable proportion of the cost may be funded by the Government, depending on the type of scheme and expenditure limits.

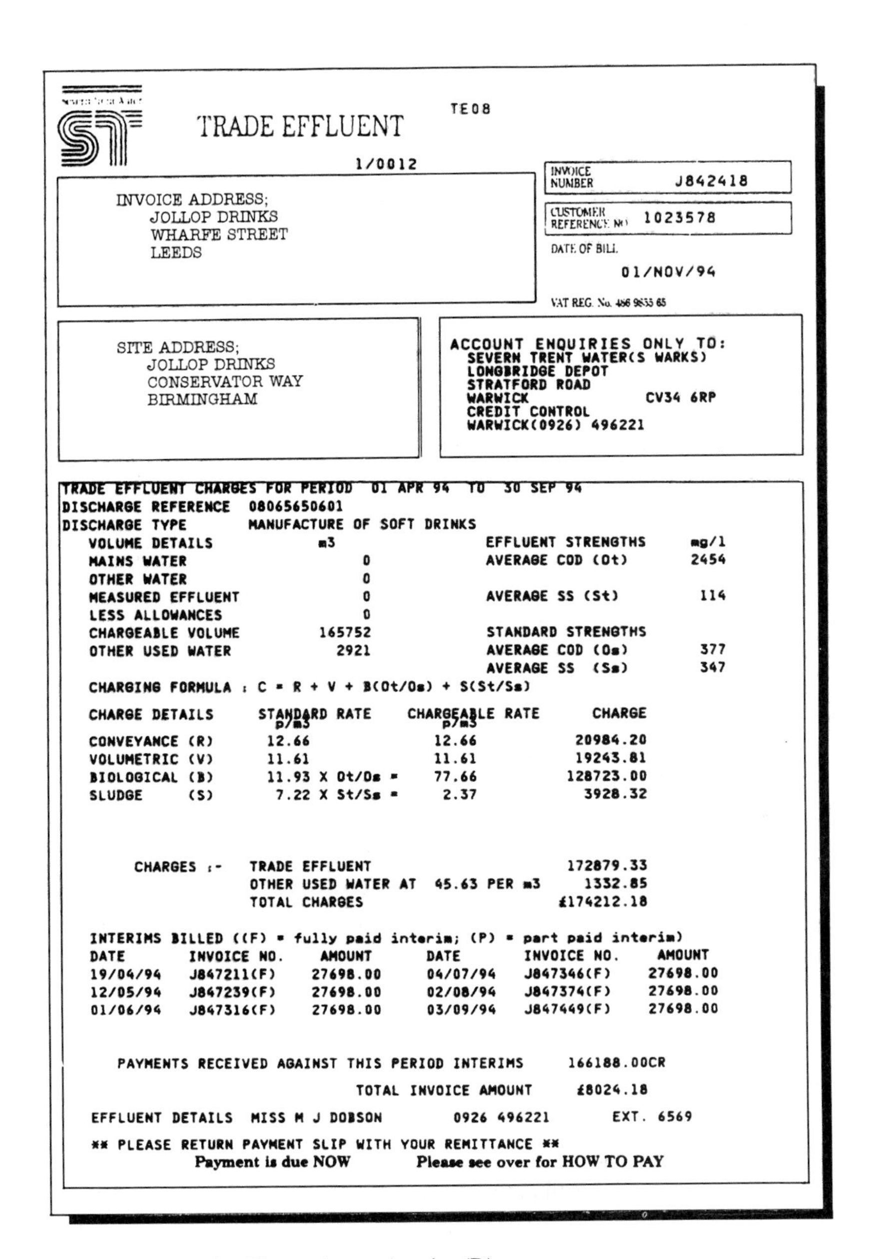

TRADE EFFLUENT TE08

1/0012

INVOICE NUMBER J842418

CUSTOMER REFERENCE NO 1023578

DATE OF BILL 01/NOV/94

VAT REG. No. 486 9855 65

INVOICE ADDRESS;
JOLLOP DRINKS
WHARFE STREET
LEEDS

SITE ADDRESS;
JOLLOP DRINKS
CONSERVATOR WAY
BIRMINGHAM

ACCOUNT ENQUIRIES ONLY TO:
SEVERN TRENT WATER(S WARKS)
LONGBRIDGE DEPOT
STRATFORD ROAD
WARWICK CV34 6RP
CREDIT CONTROL
WARWICK(0926) 496221

TRADE EFFLUENT CHARGES FOR PERIOD 01 APR 94 TO 30 SEP 94
DISCHARGE REFERENCE 08065650601
DISCHARGE TYPE MANUFACTURE OF SOFT DRINKS

VOLUME DETAILS	m3	EFFLUENT STRENGTHS	mg/l
MAINS WATER	0	AVERAGE COD (Ot)	2454
OTHER WATER	0		
MEASURED EFFLUENT	0	AVERAGE SS (St)	114
LESS ALLOWANCES	0		
CHARGEABLE VOLUME	165752	STANDARD STRENGTHS	
OTHER USED WATER	2921	AVERAGE COD (Os)	377
		AVERAGE SS (Ss)	347

CHARGING FORMULA : C = R + V + B(Ot/Os) + S(St/Ss)

CHARGE DETAILS	STANDARD RATE p/m3	CHARGEABLE RATE p/m3	CHARGE
CONVEYANCE (R)	12.66	12.66	20984.20
VOLUMETRIC (V)	11.61	11.61	19243.81
BIOLOGICAL (B)	11.93 X Ot/Os =	77.66	128723.00
SLUDGE (S)	7.22 X St/Ss =	2.37	3928.32

CHARGES :- TRADE EFFLUENT 172879.33
OTHER USED WATER AT 45.63 PER m3 1332.85
TOTAL CHARGES £174212.18

INTERIMS BILLED ((F) = fully paid interim; (P) = part paid interim)

DATE	INVOICE NO.	AMOUNT	DATE	INVOICE NO.	AMOUNT
19/04/94	J847211(F)	27698.00	04/07/94	J847346(F)	27698.00
12/05/94	J847239(F)	27698.00	02/08/94	J847374(F)	27698.00
01/06/94	J847316(F)	27698.00	03/09/94	J847449(F)	27698.00

PAYMENTS RECEIVED AGAINST THIS PERIOD INTERIMS 166188.00CR
TOTAL INVOICE AMOUNT £8024.18

EFFLUENT DETAILS MISS M J DOBSON 0926 496221 EXT. 6569

** PLEASE RETURN PAYMENT SLIP WITH YOUR REMITTANCE **
Payment is due NOW Please see over for HOW TO PAY

Figure 3.5 Trade effluent charges invoice (D).

Where there are very special drainage needs, or benefits are derived from land drainage and flood protection works, internal drainage districts have been created. The controlling boards levy direct drainage charges (rates — see Land Drainage Act 1991 ss40–54) on the occupiers of all agricultural buildings and land (which are not exempt, for instance, by reason of height above sea level) within their districts and also issue special levies on district councils to cover the non-agricultural properties.

NRA regions also have powers to levy direct general drainage charges on agricultural land outside internal drainage districts. Anglian region is currently the only one using these powers.

Some of these arrangements[4] may change with the formation of the Environment Agency.

TRADE EFFLUENT (D)

All occupiers of trade premises in England and Wales and parts of Scotland, and non-rated premises in Northern Ireland, which discharge trade effluent to a public or water undertaker's foul sewer are charged for the treatment given.

Trade effluents that are generally of a standard strength, such as from launderettes and car washes, are normally charged a set rate per cubic metre discharged. Check that the charge does reflect the effluent strength on a particular site and that the 'losses' from the mains water intake are deducted before the trade effluent charge is applied.

Figure 3.5 shows an example of a trade effluent invoice and related charge calculation. How charges have changed, significantly (!), is shown in Figure 1.2 (page 2) and their current range is given in Figure 1.4 (page 11). The charging basis (evolved from the original Mogden formula that was created in 1936 in connection with the treatment of industrial waste water at the Mogden works then serving the western part of Middlesex, UK) presently comprises, with minor variations in some parts of the country, the following elements to cover revenue expenditure (and profit in England and Wales) by the undertaker:

- *Reception (R)* — relates to expenditure on the public or water undertaker's foul sewers. The charge also covers the conveying of the effluent through the sewers;
- *Volumetric treatment of trade effluent (V)* — this covers screening, primary settlement, tertiary treatment to reduce suspended solids and all outfalls of treated sewage. The charge raised covers the net expenditure by the undertaker;
- *Biological treatment of the trade effluent (B)* — this unit of the charge, which also covers a proportion of the secondary sludge treatment (that is, after biological treatment) and disposal costs, is modified by the strength of the settled trade effluent compared with the average settled strength of the region, as chemical

oxygen demand (COD). If the trade effluent is twice the regional strength, for example, then the charge is doubled under this part of the formula. The secondary treatment costs may appear as a separate charge within the formula (*Vb* in the case of Anglian, North West, Southern, Welsh and Wessex Water which is an additional unmodified charge per cubic metre where there is biological treatment);

- *Treatment and disposal of primary sludges (S)* — primary sludge comprises the solid matter which has been settled or screened out of the raw effluent on entering the treatment works. This part of the charge is also modified by the strength of the trade effluent compared with the average strength, as suspended solids (SS), of the region. If the trade effluent is, say, half the regional SS, then the charge will be halved under this part of the formula.

The formula is usually as set out below:

$$C = R + V + \frac{Ot}{Os}B + \frac{St}{Ss}S$$

where:

C = total charge per cubic metre for the period of the account based on samples taken in that period (minimum charges apply);

Ot = trade effluent COD mg per litre, after one hour settlement at pH7, for the company being billed;

Os = regional average COD mg per litre of crude sewage after one hour quiescent settlement;

St = trade effluent SS mg per litre at pH7 for the company being billed;

Ss = regional average SS mg per litre of crude sewage.

The following worked example assumes a trade effluent COD of 1086 mg per litre, which is double the regional average, and an SS of 174 mg per litre, which is half the regional average for the particular charge period. Bear in mind that regional strengths for COD and SS can alter from year to year, thus changing the overall charge for a given strength of trade effluent.

The charges and strengths used in the example are approximately the average of those published by the ten water services plcs in England and Wales for 1995–96.

$$C = R + V + \frac{Ot}{Os}B + \frac{St}{Ss}S$$

$$C = 13.17\text{ p} + 12.72\text{ p} + \left(\frac{1086}{543} \times 18.55\text{ p}\right) + \left(\frac{174}{348} \times 11.97\text{ p}\right)$$

$$C = 13.17\text{ p} + 12.72\text{ p} + 37.10\text{ p} + 5.99\text{ p}$$

Thus $C = 69.00$ pence per cubic metre (£3.14/1000 gallons) — a 2.4-fold increase in nine years!

Some undertakers quote charges in terms of £ sterling per tonne for *B* and *S* to aid large dischargers in calculating their charge liability.

If a trade effluent is not fully treated by an undertaker, then no charge is made for the *B* and *S* elements in the formula. The usual example of this is where sewage is discharged untreated, except for screening, through a sea outfall. Guidelines, published by the Water Authorities Association in 1986, created a new sea outfall charge. The charge applies to trade effluent fed through water undertaker discharges to sea, including tidal waters. The regionally-based charge may include one or more of the following elements:

- *R* — reception and conveyance charge (for short outfalls with no additional facilities). This is the same R factor and charge as that mentioned on page 53;
- *Vm* — being a charge for the volumetric and preliminary treatment for sea outfalls which include additional headworks, pumps, tanks, etc;
- *M* — being a charge for marine costs for designated long sea outfalls and additional works — for instance, diffusers.

Obviously, trade effluent charges are a significant cost element on many industrial sites. It is most important to remember that the stronger the effluent, the greater the charge per cubic metre. On the other hand, savings can be made by:

- reducing volume;
- reducing the contents of the effluent which contribute to the COD;
- reducing the contents of the effluent which contribute to the SS.

If a company saves water on its premises but is unable to save much on COD and SS, the strength of the effluent will rise because there is less dilution. As a result, the charge per cubic metre will increase but the overall invoice total will fall, because of the reduction in volume.

Watering down effluent strength is a trap to be avoided — it will increase the overall charge, not reduce it!

The trade effluent volume is either assessed, probably using the mains water meter readings as a basis, or measured. If assessed, allowances need to be deducted for water that does not end up as trade effluent. This includes:

- water used for domestic purposes (see above);
- evaporation;
- water incorporated in a product;
- discharges other than to sewer.

If the volume is measured through a flume, for instance, ensure that the readings are accurate. The build-up of solids in or after the flume will create a falsely high reading. Regular inspection, maintenance and accuracy checks are very important. If domestic effluent or rainwater is discharged with the trade effluent, then allowances should be claimed in accordance with the water undertaker's guidelines, or by using direct measurement.

The strength of a trade effluent is assessed by sampling. If an effluent is low in volume and reasonably consistent, then the trade effluent inspector may visit only a few times over a charging period. Depending on the charging policy of the undertaker, the discharge may be put in a banded system of charges. The undertaker will wish to put the discharge in a higher cost band if the strength increases. Conversely, the discharger will wish to ask for a lower band if the strength decreases.

If a trade effluent is high in volume, strong and variable, the sampling frequency will be increased in order to get a reasonably accurate average for the period. An important point to remember, or act upon, is that the ultimate accuracy measurement is continuous sampling proportional to the flow.

If the analytical results of spot samples taken by the water undertaker are studied in relation to effluent quality, it will be noticed that the timing and number of samples can make a significant difference to effluent charges, for good or ill! If a discharger feels that the trade effluent sampling does not truly reflect the quality of the effluent, the situation can be discussed with the trade effluent inspector or someone who specializes in the subject. The site may be one of the few where biochemical oxygen demand (BOD) is a more appropriate test than COD to determine the biological element of the charge.

For the industries that do not have on-site laboratories, there are a number of easily used and portable test kits which will perform COD and many other water-related tests. Many water undertakers sell an analytical service and the names of public analysts appear in local Yellow Pages directories.

WATER RESOURCES ABSTRACTION (E)

Many commercial and industrial sites have their own source of water supply — for example, from a well, spring or river. In England and Wales, virtually all private abstractions, other than for some domestic, agricultural and a few other purposes, have to be covered by a licence which usually states the maximum hourly, daily and yearly quantity which can be taken from the source. An abstraction licence is not required in Northern Ireland or Scotland, although this may change.

On 1 April 1993, the NRA introduced a unified Scheme of Abstraction Charges to replace the ten schemes it inherited from the former Regional Water Authorities. The new Scheme provides, for the first time ever, a consistent basis for charges across England and Wales, but retains rates of charge (Standard Unit Charges, expressed as £ sterling per thousand cubic metres — £10.24 on

TABLE 3.6
Water abstraction charging factors

Source		Season		Loss	
Supported[1]	3.0	Summer	1.6	High[2]	1.0
Unsupported	1.0	Winter	0.16	Medium[3]	0.6
Tidal	0.2	All year	1.0	Low[4]	0.03
				Very low[5]	0.003

Notes:

[1] The Scheme leaflet lists these named sources (on which the NRA spends money to boost the water available).

[2] For example, spray irrigation.

[3] For example, public and private water supply.

[4] For example, non-evaporative cooling.

[5] For example, fish farms.

average for 1995/6 across the 10 regions) related to the NRA's expenditure within each of its regions.

Factors are included in the Scheme for source, season and loss so that charges reflect the relative impact of the authorized abstraction on water resources and the associated level of NRA activity as shown in Table 3.6. The NRA can only use these charges to recover their related costs.

The Scheme may appear lengthy and involved but a leaflet is published each year to advise abstractors of the current Standard Unit Charge for each Region and the basis of the Scheme. A typical account and supporting calculation is shown in Figure 3.6 on pages 58 and 59.

The water abstraction charge is levied according to the figures that appear in the Water Resources Act licence, not the amount actually abstracted. This is an important principle. The amount appearing in the licence is, as it were, reserved for the abstractor (providing nature ensures that the water is there for the taking). As water capacity is made available for the abstractor, it is reasonable that the abstractor pays for the privilege, even if the option is not fully taken up.

Section 126 of the Water Resources Act 1991 provides an abatement of charges when the abstractor has helped the NRA by constructing works or by financial or material assistance. Section 127 covers special charges in respect of spray irrigation.

A water abstraction licence should be seen as a valuable asset for any business and one which should not be lightly given away or even reduced. Because of the advertising and other procedures which surround the procurement of new, or alteration of existing, licences and the demand exceeding water availability in many areas, it is often difficult or impossible to obtain a licence for new quantities. Thus, the minimizing of abstraction charges is likely to come only as a result of permanently forfeiting part — or all — of the assets on the licence.

Some methods of improving water abstraction economics include:

- reducing the licensed quantities in line with present and expected demand (but only after very careful consideration);
- checking the charging scheme to see if there is a relationship between daily and yearly abstraction totals which affects the charge;
- considering the pattern of usage throughout the year. Can storage, or a slight change in water use in summer, allow the user to avoid being penalized for summer use?
- if the site uses mains water as well as private abstraction, and the latter is not fully utilized, consider ways in which mains water (assuming it is the more expensive source) can be replaced with abstracted water;
- should a site be up for sale, ensure that those selling the premises make the most of the abstraction licence asset.

The licensee should be careful not to lose claim to the licence. The most common pitfall is that of a change in name of the occupier of the land to which the licence refers. If the NRA is not notified within 15 months of the change, theoretically it should cancel the licence.

DIRECT DISCHARGE TO RIVERS, ETC (F)

From 1 July 1991, the NRA introduced charges to recover its relevant costs in respect of applications and consents for discharges to controlled waters in England and Wales. No such charges had been levied before. From 1 April 1994, under the Water Resources Act 1991, the NRA introduced a slightly amended scheme which has effect until 31 March 1999. The scheme attracts an application charge, to which VAT is added (the remaining charges being non-VATable) and an annual charge. The latter is very site-specific as it takes into account, through categories and factors:

- the volume (in terms of the maximum daily discharge permitted by the consent);
- the contents of the discharge (relating to the provisions in the consent and the increasingly unfriendly nature of the contents);
- the receiving waters (that is, ground, coastal, surface or estuarial).

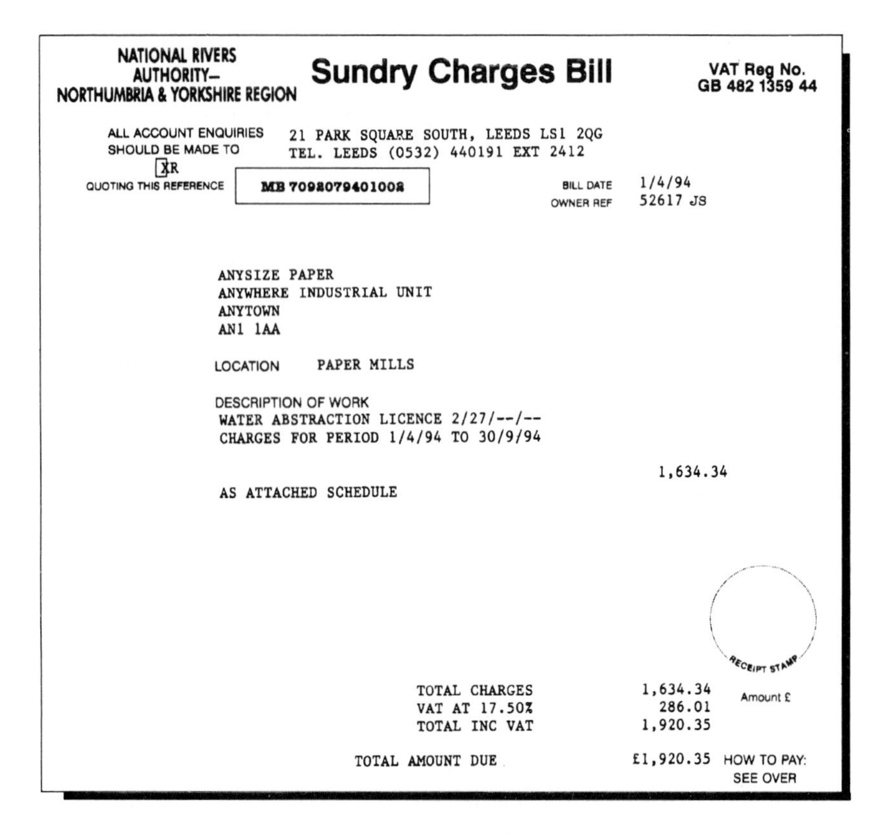
NATIONAL RIVERS AUTHORITY– NORTHUMBRIA & YORKSHIRE REGION

Sundry Charges Bill

VAT Reg No. GB 482 1359 44

ALL ACCOUNT ENQUIRIES SHOULD BE MADE TO XR — 21 PARK SQUARE SOUTH, LEEDS LS1 2QG
TEL. LEEDS (0532) 440191 EXT 2412

QUOTING THIS REFERENCE: MB 709807940100

BILL DATE 1/4/94
OWNER REF 52617 JS

ANYSIZE PAPER
ANYWHERE INDUSTRIAL UNIT
ANYTOWN
AN1 1AA

LOCATION PAPER MILLS

DESCRIPTION OF WORK
WATER ABSTRACTION LICENCE 2/27/--/--
CHARGES FOR PERIOD 1/4/94 TO 30/9/94

1,634.34

AS ATTACHED SCHEDULE

RECEIPT STAMP

TOTAL CHARGES	1,634.34
VAT AT 17.50%	286.01
TOTAL INC VAT	1,920.35

Amount £

TOTAL AMOUNT DUE £1,920.35

HOW TO PAY: SEE OVER

NRA — NORTHUMBRIA AND YORKSHIRE REGION
SCHEDULE OF WATER ABSTRACTION LICENCES AND CHARGES

Licence Number	Appl Number	Location	Authorized Abstraction TCM.
2/27/--/---		paper mill	1261.060

Water abstraction charges are levied under Section 123 of the Water Resources Act 1991. If the total amount payable for the year is less than £1000 it is due and payable on the 1st April. If the total charge is £1000 or more, then half is due on 1st April and half on 1st October when separate accounts will be issued. There is a minimum charge which has been set at £25 for the financial year 1994/95.
Type of business — paper making

Figure 3.6 Water abstraction account (E) plus related schedule.

This is inevitably rounded-off by a financial factor, which is set annually (£401 for 1995/6).

The NRA levies a charge for outfalls that are regulated under IPC (see Chapter 2 under HMIP page 21), where the NRA is the sole regulator. The charge, which is presently 56% of the normal charge, is levied to cover the environmental monitoring required.

The NRA has been keen to involve the discharger in some limited cost cutting by encouraging self-monitoring. The NRA will work with appropriate dischargers for a period before the monitoring becomes operational. Although this assumes that some dischargers can run a measuring and sampling system more cheaply than the NRA, what is far more important is that the health of the site, in terms of good housekeeping, be constantly checked through scrutiny of the monitoring results.

In April 1994, the NRA published a chart giving factor and charge comparisons for different types of discharges and locations and this is shown (with charges updated) in Table 3.7 on page 60. A leaflet is available from the NRA[5], giving the current Annual Charge Financial Factor (common throughout England and Wales) and the basis for the Scheme. An example of an account is shown in Figure 3.7 on page 61.

Charging Factors			**Chargeable Abstraction TCM**	**Standard Unit Charge £**	**Charge**	
source	**season**	**loss**			**£**	**p**
1.0	1.0	0.6	756.636	4.32	3268	67
			1ST HALF PAYMENT		1634	34
			VAT (if applicable)		286	01
			2ND HALF PAYMENT		1634	33
			VAT (if applicable)		286	00
			AMOUNT NOW DUE 1 APRIL / 1 OCTOBER		3840	68

By studying the way in which the factors increase in the charges scheme, it may be possible to alleviate the charge for a particular discharge. The volume on the consent is likely to be the main driver; thus, the cutting of water-use on site is of great importance.

TABLE 3.7
Examples of NRA charges for discharges. (Based on an NRA publication.)

Type of discharge	Volume band	Content	Receiving waters	1995/6 charge
Cooling water discharge into stream	0–5 m^3 Factor = 0.3	Band G Factor = 0.3	Surface Factor = 1.0	£36.09
Very small 'surface' water discharge into stream	0–5 m^3 Factor = 0.3	Band F Factor = 0.5	Surface Factor = 1.0	£60.15
Very small discharge of boiler blowdown (5 m^3 per day) into soakaway	1–5 m^3 Factor = 0.3	Band D Factor = 2.0	Ground Factor = 0.5	£120.30
Small sewage treatment works discharging to a stream (descriptive conditions)	5–20 m^3 Factor = 0.5	Band D Factor = 2.0	Surface Factor = 1.0	£401.00
Very small discharge of trade rinse water (4 m^3 per day) into a canal	0–5 m^3 Factor = 0.3	Band B Factor = 5.0	Surface Factor = 1.0	£601.50
Restaurant/pub sewage treatment plant discharge (10 m^3 per day with numeric condition)	5–20 m^3 Factor = 0.5	Band C Factor = 3.0	Surface Factor = 1.0	£601.50
Small discharge of vehicle wash water (15 m^3 per day) into a river	5–20 m^3 Factor = 0.5	Band B Factor = 5.0	Surface Factor = 1.0	£1002.50
Large discharge from a works with organic trade wastes discharging into an estuary	50,000–150,000 m^3 Factor = 9.0	Band A Factor = 14.0	Estuary Factor = 1.5	£75,789
Very large discharge from chemical site to a river	>150,000 m^3 Factor = 14.0	Band A Factor = 14.0	Surface Factor = 1.0	£78,596

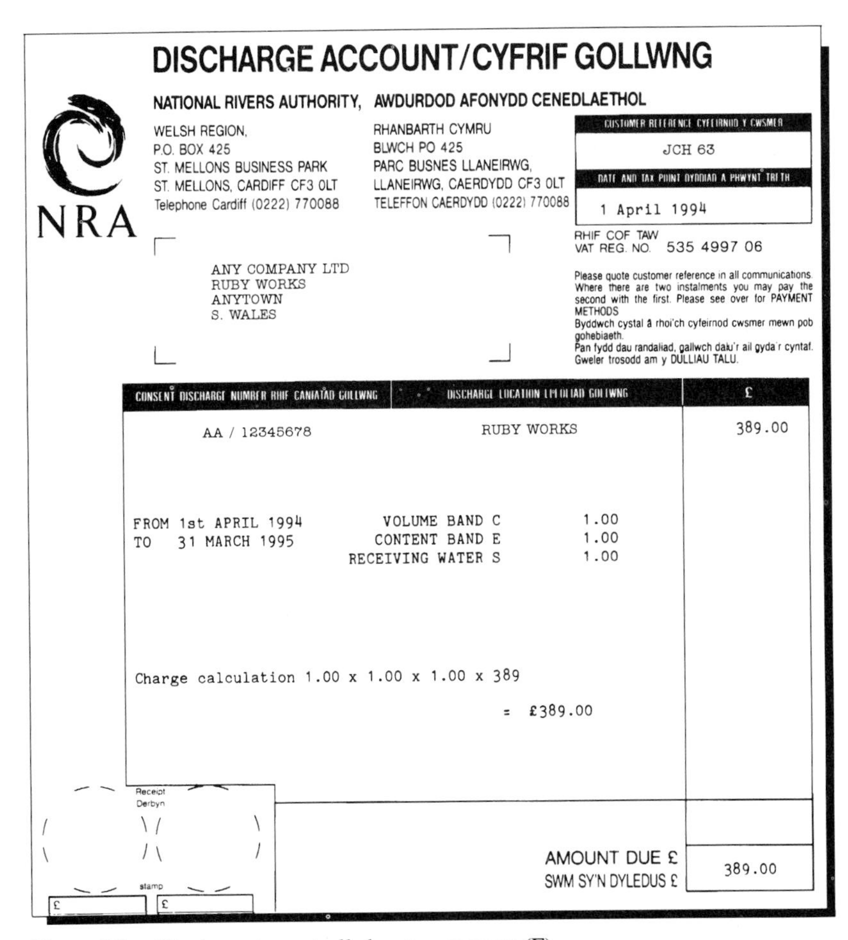

DISCHARGE ACCOUNT/CYFRIF GOLLWNG

NRA

NATIONAL RIVERS AUTHORITY, AWDURDOD AFONYDD CENEDLAETHOL

WELSH REGION,
P.O. BOX 425
ST. MELLONS BUSINESS PARK
ST. MELLONS, CARDIFF CF3 0LT
Telephone Cardiff (0222) 770088

RHANBARTH CYMRU
BLWCH PO 425
PARC BUSNES LLANEIRWG,
LLANEIRWG, CAERDYDD CF3 0LT
TELEFFON CAERDYDD (0222) 770088

CUSTOMER REFERENCE CYFEIRNOD Y CWSMER
JCH 63

DATE AND TAX POINT DYDDIAD A PHWYNT TRETH
1 April 1994

RHIF COF TAW
VAT REG. NO. 535 4997 06

ANY COMPANY LTD
RUBY WORKS
ANYTOWN
S. WALES

Please quote customer reference in all communications. Where there are two instalments you may pay the second with the first. Please see over for PAYMENT METHODS
Byddwch cystal â rhoi'ch cyfeirnod cwsmer mewn pob gohebiaeth.
Pan fydd dau randaliad, gallwch dalu'r ail gyda'r cyntaf. Gweler trosodd am y DULLIAU TALU.

CONSENT DISCHARGE NUMBER RHIF CANIATÂD GOLLWNG	DISCHARGE LOCATION LLEOLIAD GOLLWNG	£
AA / 12345678	RUBY WORKS	389.00

FROM 1st APRIL 1994
TO 31 MARCH 1995

VOLUME BAND C	1.00
CONTENT BAND E	1.00
RECEIVING WATER S	1.00

Charge calculation 1.00 x 1.00 x 1.00 x 389

= £389.00

Receipt
Derbyn
stamp

£ £

AMOUNT DUE £
SWM SY'N DYLEDUS £ 389.00

Figure 3.7 Discharge to controlled waters account (F).

ENVIRONMENTAL MONITORING AND PROTECTION

From Table 3.1 on page 39 it can be seen that environmental monitoring and protection costs are not levied directly on the customer. When the domestic rating system was discontinued in England and Wales the charges were abolished. The NRA now receives, as a replacement, grant-in-aid from the Government (that is, money from the general taxpayer) to cover general activities of water quality control, pollution prevention and the provision of leisure facilities.

SOURCES OF INFORMATION

REFERENCES IN CHAPTER 3

1. Centre for the Study of Regulated Industries (CRI) — a research centre of the Chartered Institute of Public Finance and Accountancy — publishers of comprehensive annual surveys of United Kingdom water industry charges and costs — for example, *Water Charges 1994/95* and *Water Services and Costs 1992/93*.
2. *1995–96 Report on Tariff Structures and Charges*, 1995 (OFWAT).
3. *NRA Water Resources Strategy Document*, 1993 (NRA).
4. *Land Drainage and Flood Defence Responsibilities, 2nd edition* , 1993 (Institution of Civil Engineers). Updated to include legislation applicable to England and Wales enacted up to 31 December 1992.
5. *NRA Scheme of Charges in Respect of Applications and Consents for Discharges to Controlled Waters*, 1994 (NRA).

4. REDUCING WATER CONSUMPTION FOR DOMESTIC PURPOSES

The domestic areas of water use on an industrial or commercial site include washrooms, toilets, canteens and drinking fountains. Water used in, and effluent discharged from, these areas are administered in a different way from factory process water and trade effluent (see Chapters 2 and 3).

There are important reasons for devoting time and thought to the domestic areas of a site. In offices and shops most of the water used is for domestic purposes. In large premises significant costs are incurred and correspondingly significant savings can be made[1]. Another reason relates to factory sites. If staff are accustomed to strict controls in terms of water and effluent savings on the factory floor, it would seem logical to introduce similar controls for the domestic areas. In the same way, if the employees are aware of the importance of water saving in the domestic areas of the factory, they are more likely to take the message with them onto the factory floor.

Before looking at some of the ways in which savings can be achieved, the point should be made that measures implemented must not be too extreme[2]. The welfare and health of staff, or the public, should not be put at risk.

It may also be worthwhile reflecting on recent Australian research, quoted by OFWAT, which found that domestic customers fell into four different water use groups: Conservers, Consumers, Gardeners and Pretenders:

- more than a third were Conservers — they believe in and practice water conservation in their daily lives;
- water Consumers made up a quarter — they take water for granted and assume it is available in abundance;
- the Gardeners totalled just under a quarter — this group support water conservation in principle, providing their gardens do not suffer;
- Pretenders made up the remainder — they give lip service to the idea of water conservation, but their attitudes and habits indicate they make no effort to conserve water in practice.

REGULAR MAINTENANCE

A plumber spent a week in a school, checking pipework, re-washering taps and overhauling cisterns. As a result, water consumption dropped over 60%, from 90 to 33 cubic metres per week[3,4]. This illustrates the benefits to be gained from regular maintenance. Incidentally, a high pressure system is available for injecting a sealing compound into existing threaded pipe joints — the user needs to be satisfied that the sealer is compatible with the liquid in the pipe.

METERING

Before considering water-saving devices, it is advisable to investigate how the domestic consumption is paid for and how much water is used in domestic areas.

If payment is still based on rateable value, it may be argued that the payment is not related directly to water use and, as a result, there is no incentive to cut water bills. But, if a company wishes its employees to be careful in their use of resources, then water (a resource) and effluent (a negative resource) should not be treated differently.

If domestic water is not paid for by metered supply, assuming that it comes from a water undertaker, then the daily or weekly consumption is unlikely to be known. More importantly, the company may be paying more than necessary by not opting for a metered supply. This option should certainly be investigated as a first step. Premises with high rateable values in relation to the number of occupants will benefit from paying by metered consumption.

Even if water comes from a private source, it is worth considering the installation of a meter[5]. On small service pipes from water mains, a meter installation can be easily achieved if there is an existing stopvalve before the water-using appliances (see Figure 4.1).

Meters should be installed in positions where they can be read easily, or else be provided with a remote read-out. (Trials are underway, in the UK, to read mains water meters via the telephone network.) Readings should be taken daily or weekly, depending on the extent of domestic water use, and the results cross-checked and plotted graphically in terms of water use and cost. Changes in the pattern of water use require investigation. If readings are taken before water-saving devices are fitted, then the impact of the measures should show up on the graph.

The Audit Commission occasional paper on water services in the National Health Service (NHS)[6] (from which information has been taken for use elsewhere in this book) reports the development of a performance indicator to measure water consumption in hospitals. This is expressed in litres per patient bed day. This approach can be adapted to the metered domestic areas of most sites. Staff should be informed when meters are installed. Only 3% of staff in a group of hospitals visited in the Midlands, as part of the above investigation, were aware that hospitals were metered for water and thus the cost was based on the amount consumed.

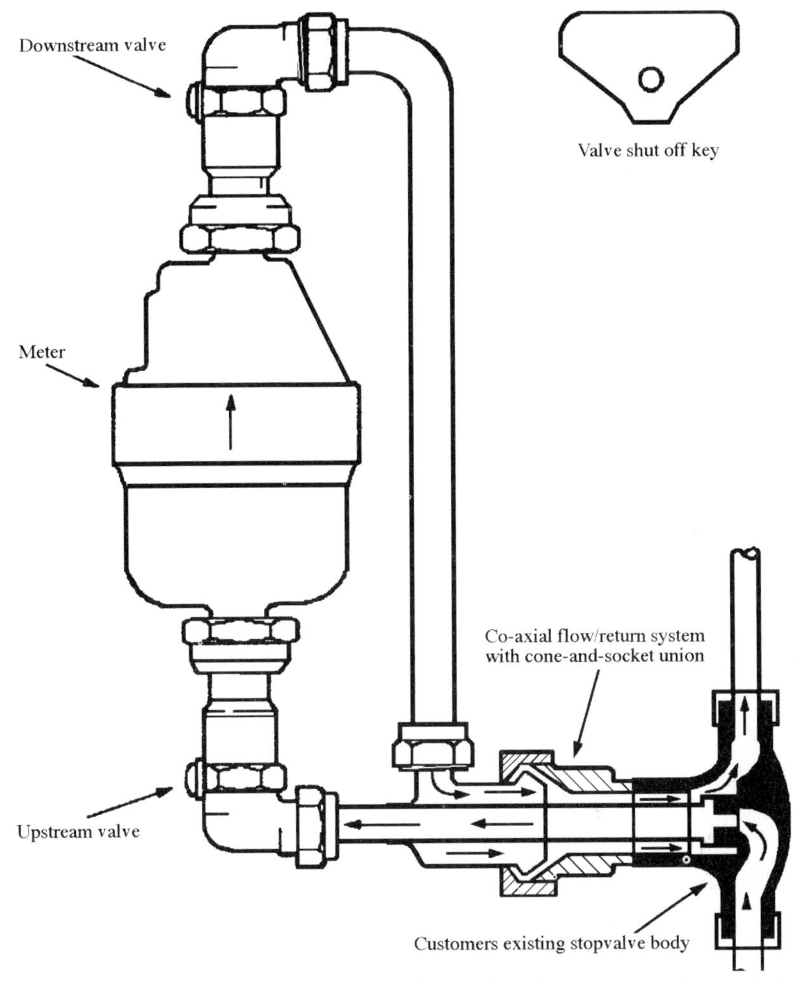

Figure 4.1 Stopvalve water metering coupling device. (Source: Mater Options Ltd and WASK–RMF Ltd.)

Despite a meter being installed, the owners of a sports goods shop were still unaware that a hot water heater in the kitchen was leaking at a rate of 0.75 litres per minute and an avoidable cost of £340 per year.

An unexpectedly high reading on a meter may not always be due to a new leak. If the water pressure has reduced, allowing air into the pipework, it is possible to get 'air spin' in some types of meter as a result of the air being forced out of the system.

WATER SAVING DEVICES

If an organization is considering the installation of water-saving devices, it is important to know what is available and where it can be obtained. The investment may well have a payback of less than 12 months. In the UK there is a voluntary scheme for testing fittings and materials, to check that they are suitable for connection to the mains (it does not test fitness for purpose). These approved items and relevant information and addresses appear in the *Water Fittings and Materials Directory*[7]. It contains most of the items described here.

FLOW CONTROL VALVES

Sometimes described as flow restrictors or constant flow valves, flow control valves perform an automatic regulating task when the water pressure to a piece of equipment varies[8]. For a given outlet size, the flow of water increases as the pressure increases. Thus, if it normally takes one minute to perform a task properly using five litres of water, and the mains pressure then increases by 50% (the task still taking one minute), then about six litres will have flowed at the higher pressure. The extra litre represents a wastage of water.

Where there are many small water-using points it is worthwhile fitting suitable flow control valves. A survey in a six-storey London hotel showed that it would be possible to save just over £50 per room per year in metered water charges for all but the top floor. Together with the reduced charge for getting rid of the water to the sewer, the saving would be £100 per room per year.

A district general hospital fitted tap restrictors to over 2500 hot and cold taps, reducing the flow from 20–25 litres to 12 litres of water per minute. The payback was achieved in ten months.

A flow monitor is available which memorizes normal patterns of water use through a meter and sounds an alarm and/or shuts off the supply if a leak or burst is suspected. The water can also be shut off by the turn of a switch on the unit.

PRESSURE REDUCING VALVES

Pressure reducing valves, also known as pressure limiting valves, reduce the pressure downstream of the device to a pre-set level. In this case there is no restriction on flow, except the normal upper flow limit which is governed by the capacity of the pipework and the water-using device. This type of valve should be fitted when the water pressure is too high and it is not desired to control the flow of water to a constant amount. By reducing the pressure, less water flows through the system over a given period and less is lost through any undiscovered leaks.

SHOWERS

Depending on the design and application, showers may use much less water than baths. Savings of 55% to 90% have been quoted. As hot water is usually involved, heating bills are reduced by a similar percentage. In hard water areas it pays to investigate the use of softened water — those using the shower will prefer it and the fine holes in the spray will not become blocked by scale. For further water savings, a delayed closing valve can be fitted which requires pushing every half minute to maintain the water flow to the shower head. When designing new or refurbishing existing buildings containing baths, consider reducing the number of baths and increasing the provision of showers.

SPRAY TAPS

Taps are available in a form which produces a fine spray. Savings of 40% for cold and over 80% for hot water are quoted (see also 'Waste Plugs', page 69). The way in which taps are controlled also repays study. Models are available which are foot operated, or lever operated using the arm or the knee. Alternatively, delayed closing or timed flow (about 15 seconds) spray taps can be fitted. Taps activated by infrared sensors are also available.

If spray taps cannot be fitted, consider using taps which incorporate aerators (but not on drinking water taps).

URINAL FLUSHING CONTROLS

A number of control assemblies have come on to the market for automatic flushing cisterns. Besides the basic economic reason for fitting such devices, the Water Bye-laws[9,10] require the phasing out of the continuous flow arrangement for topping up automatic flushing cisterns. It is obviously a cause of waste when the water flows all day and every day, irrespective of the use, or lack of use, of the urinals. Water savings of up to 90% are quoted. The control devices are capable of responding to the entry of people into the immediate area of the urinal, or to the use of water in nearby hand basins. Six of these valves were fitted in the domestic areas of an engineering company to the west of London. At the same time, flow restrictors were inserted in the pipework serving wash basin taps. The combined effect was to reduce the water usage from 25,000 gallons to 6000 gallons per week on average. Thus, an outlay of about £500 in the early 1980s has resulted in water and sewerage savings which are now estimated at over £3000 a year. Weekly inspections ensure that the savings are maintained.

A urinal in an accident and emergency department toilet was wrongly fitted with a lever-operated float valve which had been left fully open. The flow rate was nine litres per minute, costing the hospital £110 per week.

The University Hospital of Wales introduced automatically controlled flushing cisterns in the gentlemen's washrooms, with a saving of over £20,000 per year and a six-month payback.

WASTE PLUGS

For those who require a full basin of water for washing there is often the problem in public places of finding a plug to stop the water running to waste, despite Water Bye-laws requiring that plugs be provided (unless water is supplied by a spray tap). To overcome this problem, there exist pop-up plugs or specially designed vandal-resistant swivel plugs that can be rotated by hand in any direction to an open or closed position. When the waste is associated with a shower or with spray taps or fittings which deliver water to a basin, at a rate not exceeding 3.6 litres per minute (about 0.8 gallons per minute), no plug is required under the present Water Bye-laws.

A French utility company is to experiment with a treatment and recycling facility for discharges from baths and sinks located in two buildings of a university campus.

WATER CLOSET CISTERNS

On average, nine litres (two gallons) of perfectly good drinking water (32% of average UK household use) are used to flush away the contents of the WC pan. The combined average mains water and sewerage charge for the nine litres is now just one new penny per flush (yes, we do spend a penny!). This water use is a good candidate for suitable clean reusable water[11,12]. In an emergency any acceptable waste water may be pressed into service, but in normal circumstances it seems natural to reuse fairly clear water.

The Tokyo Metropolitan area has strict regulations on recycling water, particularly in tower blocks. On average, those over eight storeys are required to install self-contained facilities for treatment. District water recycling centres provide recycled water at a lower cost than the municipal charge.

The Compagnie des Eaux de Paris has piloted a mini-treatment plant in a residential building. The raw effluent is biologically treated, microfiltered using membranes and then decolourized using activated carbon. The non-potable liquid can be reused for toilet flushing, washing cars or watering lawns, but on no account must there be any cross-connection between the mains water plumbing system and the pipework carrying the 'grey water'.

If mains water is used, consider reducing the amount of water used per flush. Dual flushing cisterns may again be allowed. The result of their use should be water savings, but there has been experience of blocked drains (due to the lower volume discharged), and decreased hygiene. They could even lead to an increase in water use unless a clear notice large enough for the purpose is displayed to explain the need, for instance, to hold the lever down for more water. Selecting the wrong quantity on the first flush means a second try and a waste of water. Note that the Water Bye-laws do not allow dual-flush cisterns. Instead, the Bye-laws require the introduction of a flush of 7.5 litres for new cisterns installed after December 1992. Six-litre models are available.

During the 1985–86 winter, the Southampton General Hospital placed housebricks, sealed from the water by a plastic bag, in 300 toilet cisterns in public areas (not wards). The aim was to cut consumption because the hospital was £26,000 over its annual £180,000 water budget. If a brick is too large for the cisterns, then a suitable substitute is gravel in a plastic bag, or water in a sealed plastic bag. However, the water supply industry does not approve of *ad hoc* means of reducing flushing volumes, as they can be counterproductive.

Cistern dams to control the volume of flushed water are available from companies such as Rentokil. Fitting a WC dam can save up to 40% of the volume of each flush. Any such arrangement must ensure that the design of the pan is capable of clearing the pan contents with the reduced quantity of flushing water and will not lead to blocked drains.

A simple modification, involving a small tube, has been produced which enables the user to flush only as much water as is needed — when the handle is released, the flow stops. This saves water but, before fitting the device, it is necessary to check that it is acceptable to those who are likely to use the toilet.

SOURCES OF INFORMATION

REFERENCES IN CHAPTER 4

1. Department of the Environment, 1993, *Water Use in Accommodation and Estates Work, Environmental Action Guide Advisory Note 4* (HMSO). Contains sections on flushing toilets, urinals (includes cost-saving statistics), water saving devices, maintenance, leakage, etc.
2. *BS 6700: 1987 British Standard Specification for Design, Installation, Testing and Maintenance of Services Supplying Water for Domestic Use within Buildings and their Curtilages* (British Standards Institution).
3. Department for Education, 1993, *Managing School Facilities Guide 1 — Saving Water* (HMSO).
4. Messer, J. and Parker, J., 1989, Water torture, *The Times Educational Supplement*, 31 March, 29.
5. *BS 7405: 1991 Guide to Selection and Application of Flowmeters for the Measurement of Fluid Flow in Closed Circuits* (British Standards Institution). Also deals with secondary instrumentation and some aspects of calibration.

6. Audit Commission, 1993, *Untapped Savings: Water Services in the NHS, NHS Occasional Papers Number 5* (HMSO).
7. WRc Evaluation and Testing Centre, biannual, *Water Fittings and Materials Directory* (Unwin Brothers).
8. British Valve and Actuator Manufacturer's Association, 8th Floor, Bridge House, 121 Smallbrook, Queensway, Birmingham B5 4JP, tel: 0121 643 3377, fax: 0121 643 5064. The trade association for manufacturers of valves and actuators.
9. *Water Supply Bye-laws Guide*,1989 (Ellis Horwood).
10. Water utility, water company, DoENI or Scottish Region bye-laws.
11. Douglas-Bate, R., 1992, *A Guide to Living with Less Water*. Available direct from the author, Rupert Douglas-Bate, Box 2, Southend, Reading, Berks RG7 6UA. Covers saving water in the home, rainwater harvesting and soil improvements.
12. Fewkes and Turton, 1994, Recovering rainwater for WC flushing, *Environmental Health*, 102 (2): 42–46.

5. REDUCING WATER CONSUMPTION FOR PROCESS PURPOSES

It is impossible to list all the process uses for water in industry and commerce. There are, however, many applications which are common to a large number of industries and some of these are listed in Figure 5.1. A short description follows for each application, with some ideas of how savings can be made. Remember that many water-using items of plant were not designed with water efficiency in mind.

STORAGE

Many premises do not have a storage tank for incoming water. This is mostly for historical reasons, and because in the past storage has not been required by

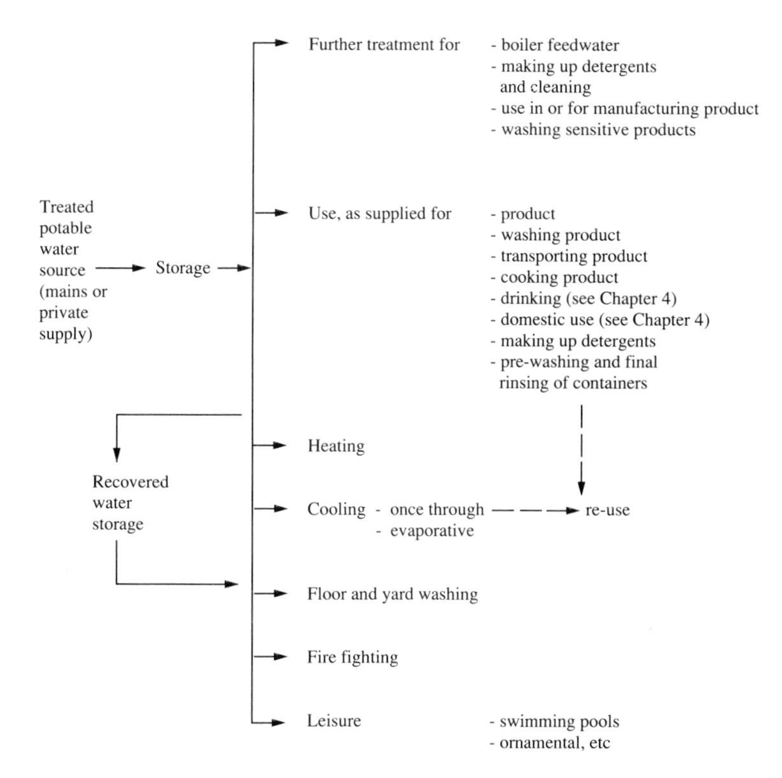

Figure 5.1 Some general uses for water within factories.

water undertakers. Storage, besides being a worthwhile form of protection and insurance, is also likely to be a requirement by a water undertaker before a metered connection is provided. If storage already exists, is it adequate for the demands made on it by the process? When the tank is full, does it overflow? Overflows cost money and may well contravene Water Bye-laws, apart from being a visual sign of a lax attitude or a hard pressed maintenance staff. Overflows can and should be stopped by rectifying a faulty ball valve seating, or adjusting the shut-off level and, if necessary, adding the protection of a fail-safe sensor. For large discharges, which presently relieve excess pipeline pressure at the inlet to water storage reservoirs, there are now 'microstations' (tiny 2 metre by 1.2 metre electricity generating devices) which can turn the excess energy back into saleable electricity[1].

If a process demands good quality water, then regular inspection and cleaning of storage facilities are essential. Depending on its construction, the tank may develop leaks and be in need of repair. Contamination may be caused by dead birds and silt can accumulate, harbouring unwanted bacteria and thus speeding corrosion.

If the storage tank is let into the ground, the inspection must be carried out with particular care. Underground tanks have been the source of serious contamination, due to the entry of contaminated water though cracks in walls of the tank or through ill-fitting access covers.

The reason for giving attention to the condition of the tank is that it can be the origin of microbiological problems throughout the factory. This in turn can lead to product losses.

If a substantial new storage facility is to be installed, consideration should be given to providing two separate, but interconnected, tanks instead of one large one. The tanks do not have to be of equal size. Draining down for inspection and maintenance is easier (and consequently more likely to be done) because the site can be kept supplied from the other tank.

Many factories add chlorine to the water on its way to a storage tank and use the tank to ensure a contact time of, say, 20 to 30 minutes[2]. In order to control the contact time, the water can be channelled through the tank using baffles (see Figure 5.2). Too many storage tanks that are used as contact tanks do not contain baffles and, worse still, do not have the outlet as far away from the inlet as possible, as it should be, in order to prevent short-circuiting.

RECOVERED WATER STORAGE

The storage of recovered water is likely to be one of the most important items of plant to help achieve water and effluent cost reductions. When justifying the

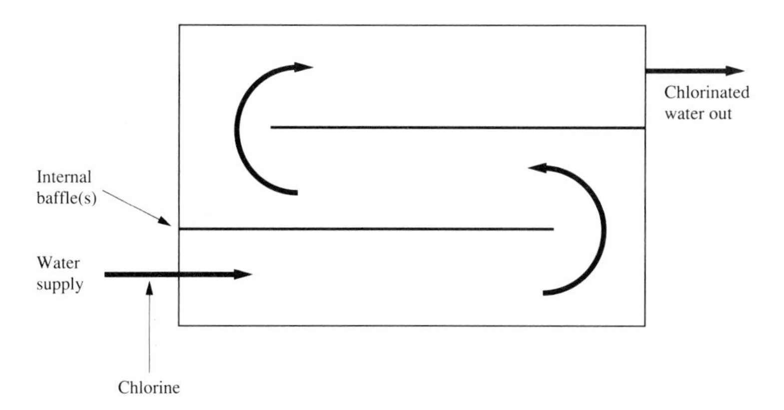

Figure 5.2 Baffled storage and chlorine contact tank.

cost for such storage, it should be easy to work out the value of the water, effluent and, perhaps, heat which will be saved. Further savings also arise due to the storage acting as a focus for other reusable waste streams, but these savings are more difficult to quantify.

A brewery uses hot liquor tanks to store hot mains water, which has been used for cooling wort, before reuse as mash and sparging liquor in the mash tun.

The dairy industry treats for reuse product condensate which has been discharged from multi-effect evaporators[3].

The manufacturers of hollow plastic balls that are used as a floating cover for liquids, especially in open tanks, claim that the product can reduce heat loss by 75%, evaporation by 87% and atmospheric pollution by 98%.

Similar basic precautions to those listed under 'Storage' are needed. In addition, however, it is necessary to guard against further risks.

CONTAMINATION

Contamination is an almost inevitable threat when water has already performed one cycle though an item of plant. Heat exchangers can leak from the product part into the coolant, and mishaps can occur in most water-using processes. Where there is any risk of contamination, which could be detrimental to the subsequent water reuse, then alarm or automatic diversion devices (to drain) should be fitted. Monitors are available to check, continuously and automatically, on pH, turbidity, conductivity, density, suspended solids and, of course, temperature; all of these have been found to be useful indicators of unsatisfactory water quality.

MISUSE

One simple precaution against misuse is to ensure that all service pipework and tanks are separately labelled or colour coded.

TEMPERATURE

It may well be attractive in terms of cost saving to reuse warm water, but this provides a perfect environment for bacterial growth and hot water dispels the benefits of chlorination more rapidly. The increasing incidence of legionnaire's disease has resulted in precautions being taken thoughout buildings, including storage facilities, to minimize the risk of further outbreaks[4,5]. Advice being given states that, besides keeping the water distribution system clean, water temperatures between 20°C and 45°C should be avoided — for example, by storing water below 20°C or at a minimum of 60°C and circulating it at 50°C, in order not to encourage the growth of the *Legionella* micro-organism[6]. For temporary storage at 55°C or above, adequate time must be allowed to ensure that the organism does not survive. Survival is improbable over 70°C, thus hot water handling equipment could periodically be subjected to this temperature. Care must also be taken to avoid the risk of scalding personnel.

It is important to select carefully the discharge point for reclaimed water. A simple investigation at an artificial fibre plant in Canada resulted in the rectification of a mistake and the saving of a considerable sum of money in operating costs. Millions of gallons of river water were pumped daily to the factory, to be used first as cooling water in services and process plant and then recovered (as warm water) for other process uses after further steam heating. Due to varying off-take demand, the cold water pressure fluctuated, sometimes wildly, and a pressure relief valve was installed. Instead of being directed to drain, as was intended, the relief water was discharged into the recovered warm water tank thus causing a near-continuous overflow to drain. As a result, the tank was always full of cold river water, which put a massive extra load on the secondary heaters to bring it up to process temperature. All this was happening under automatic control in a remote corner of the factory site, and consequently went undetected for many years. When the mistake was discovered the valve discharge was diverted to drain, with a plan to control the losses in future by varying the speed of the river water pump. The estimated saving at the time of rectification was $250,000 a year.

PUMPS[7]

The ratio of capital-to-electricity costs in the cost of ownership of a pumpset has been put at about 20:80. Thus, the initial efficiency of a pumpset and, of equal importance, its continuing efficiency has a direct impact on costs.

For larger pumps it is possible to fit instrumentation based on the thermodynamic method of pump efficiency measurement. Energy losses in pumping result in a temperature rise in the fluid being pumped. Thus, this type of monitoring is independent of any measurement of the fluid flow or power drawn.

Wherever possible:

- site the pump impellers below the level of the liquid to be pumped, thus avoiding problems with priming and loss of suction;
- let gravity do the work instead of a pump.

TREATMENT PLANT

Chapter 6 concentrates on treatment plants. For treated uses that are mentioned here, there must be a target water quality which the treatment plant should meet. It follows that, in order to control operating costs, the plant must be chosen correctly and kept running at a high level of efficiency.

BOILER FEEDWATER

There are plenty of publications available covering the operation of boilers. Water treatment is necessary to prevent corrosion and the formation of scale. Having gone to the trouble of treating boiler water, which eventually ends up as condensate, every effort should be made to return as much condensate as possible to the feed tank. Savings are thus made in water treatment and fuel costs.

Performance monitoring and testing of steam traps over seven years at two ICI works provided information for a revised engineering design guide[8]. Mechanical type traps performed well under light and heavy loads, whereas thermostatic types tended to back-up condensate as load increased.

As factory engineers know, a steam leak gives the impression that far more steam is being lost than is the case. This may have some advantages. If monetary value is allocated to leaks, this should ensure that they are given the right priority. Figure 5.3 on page 76 shows the cost per year of different lengths of steam plume for a 7 bar (100 psig) steam system supplied from an oil-fired boiler. The cost is based on fuel oil at 22 pence per litre and a boiler efficiency of 75%.

The installation of a steam-trap leak detection system alerted a works manager to widespread steam-trap failures. The symptom was the bursting of screens that protected the traps. The cause was the higher quality water from a new boiler water treatment plant, which had descaled the pipework to such an extent that the strainers could not cope.

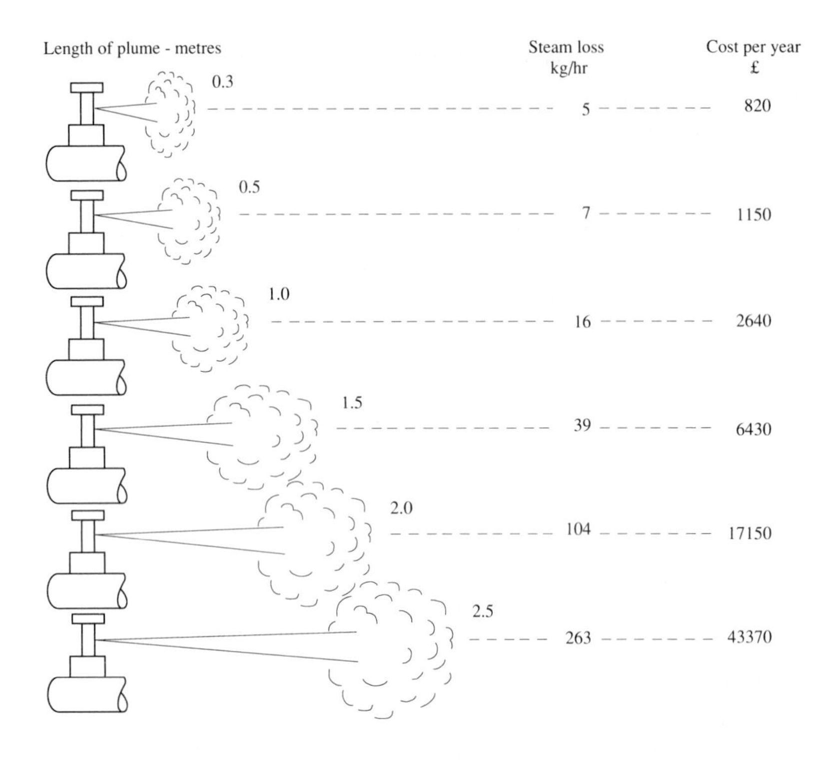

Figure 5.3 Cost of steam leaks (assuming 7 bar steam pressure). (Reproduced from *The Energy Saver*[9].)

An unavoidable loss of feedwater and heat occurs when the boiler is blown down in order to control the level of dissolved and suspended solids. Excessive blowdown should be avoided and, if the installation is suitable, recovery of part of the heat in the blowdown is possible. This can be achieved using an automatic control system which monitors the total dissolved solids (TDS) in the water inside the boiler. The blowdown valve is opened and closed automatically to maintain an optimum TDS level. Further savings can be made from a heat recovery system which captures the waste heat from the blowdown and returns it to the boiler feedwater tank. Calculations for an installation in a Scottish brewery predicted energy savings of about £5000 per year.

It makes sense if some parts of a new or existing factory installation escape the normally strict economic payback requirements of industry. One example is a condensate return system which may cost more than the apparent value of the condensate returned. Despite this, the pipework provided represents a facility which will draw to it new sources of condensate as, inevitably, the factory changes. A simple analogy is where a mass of papers accumulates in an office because there is no file in which to put them. Create files and there is more chance that the papers will be put away. This simple theme applies just as much to condensate and to recovered water systems.

MAKING UP DETERGENTS AND CLEANING

It is possible to receive naturally soft water in some areas and to use specially formulated detergents in hard water areas. If cleaning is to be more than a very minor activity, naturally soft or artificially softened water is to be recommended for detergent make-up and rinse waters. Made-up detergents and some rinses are used hot, and temporary hardness in the detergent or the rinsewater will deposit out in the detergent tank, the heat exchanger or on the plant to be cleaned, with undesirable consequences for cost and cleanliness. When hardness is deposited on the plant being cleaned, it enables product deposits to adhere more easily. On one cleaning duty, which employed two hot circulation cleans per day, it was shown that satisfactory results could be obtained with one hot and one cold clean per day. Other tests have shown that an intermediate clean can extend the use of the plant to be cleaned, thus improving processing costs.

Detergents formulated for use with very hard water can be 50% more expensive than detergents made up for soft or moderately soft water. Some detergents are more efficient than others, thus allowing cleaning to be less frequent. Many formulated detergents contain substances, such as phosphorous, which are harmful to the environment if discharged untreated. However, recent work suggests that alternative builders for laundry detergent formulations have a similar environmental impact to phosphates. Phosphate recovery plants are now in operation at three sewage treatment works in The Netherlands. The calcium phosphate pellets have been found to be an excellent raw material for the production of phosphoric acid which, in turn, can be used in fertilizers and detergents! The urban waste water treatment directive[10,11] addresses this issue, as does other UK legislation. Many detergents contribute significantly to the COD of raw effluents. Analysis of the COD of detergents in use throughout a site can be revealing and help determine the best use of these products.

VARIOUS TIPS AND CASE STUDIES

Orange peel has been used by a Liverpool company as the basis for an environmentally-friendly product for cleaning surfaces contaminated with anything which has a mineral oil base, such as tar, grease, carbon and bitumen.

Foam cleaning is an established method of detergent application in the food industry. The air device produces an instant foam which will last for 10–15 minutes. The soiling and the detergent are rinsed away easily and, because the foam is not long lasting, it does not affect the operation of any subsequent effluent treatment process. Gels are also available which work on the same principle, but without the use of air. The gel is produced chemically and is said to achieve a more intimate contact with the surface to be cleaned.

When parts of a machine have to be dismantled for cleaning, they can be cleaned in a simple washing machine. This has been proved to be an excellent money saver and a means of maintaining hygiene quality.

Where detergents can be reused, keep a keen eye on the amount of dilution which takes place. A consultant to the food industry aims for no more than a 10% loss of detergent per clean. He has experienced dilutions up to 75% in badly controlled plants. Poorly designed or operated cleaning systems cause product quality failures. The key elements for good cleaning are: time, temperature, flow velocity and chemical concentration.

Where hot water is used for plant disinfection, for instance in plate heat exchangers, the water should be soft; this is dealt with later in this chapter.

Sterilization by hot water, or a cold chlorine-based solution, has been successfully replaced by a solution of peracetic acid (PAA), with savings in water, effluent, energy and time.

Cleaning systems which serve a number of plant items are usually engineered to serve the farthest plant item. Thus, items nearest the system could use more water, heat and detergent than is necessary. A control programme needs to be provided for each circuit so that the use of water, detergent and energy can be made as efficient as possible. 'Burst rinsing', followed by adequate scavenge time, is effective and reduces water consumption. It has been estimated that 75% more water is used with continuous rinsing, with solids remaining in the vessel being cleaned at the end of the rinsing period, because the vessel never completely empties.

The use of a 'pig' for pushing out a viscous product from pipelines, prior to cleaning, can make a marked improvement in effluent quality and the profit and loss account.

The fine holes in spray balls should be protected from blockage by an in-line filter on the discharge from the detergent pump. Pressure gauges can give an indication of spray-ball and filter blockage. Pay particular attention to installations containing rotating sprays, which display a similar pressure whether the spray is rotating or not.

Bass Brewers Ltd, Cardiff, used its portable monitoring equipment (non-invasive ultrasonic flow meter, data-logger, temperature sensors and conductivity probe) to investigate cleaning-sets around the site with a view to minimizing rinse times and highlighting any lack of control. They found that the set for the Bright Beer Tank, which was manually controlled, ran for an average of 50 instead of the required 15 minutes for the final rinse, equating to a loss of

£4000 per year. By placing a pH probe in the return branch to the detergent tank and a valve to drain, and providing the operator with a timer, it was possible for the pump to be shut down three minutes after the final rinse water reached a pH of 7. The cost of the equipment was £1800, giving a payback of 5.5 months. As a result, the technique is being installed on other cleaning sets.

CLEANING-IN-PLACE (CIP)

It is now standard practice in automated cleaning-in-place (CIP) systems to reuse final rinse water as a pre-rinse. This reuses the water, the heat and a trace of detergent. In food factories the final rinse water should be of a high microbiological standard, with a free chlorine residual present. If it is reclaimed, then the reclaim tank should be inspected and cleaned regularly, to prevent a build-up of unwanted deposits. A well-commissioned CIP unit allows the water reclaim tank to overflow regularly, in order to keep it fresh, as a result of controlled flushing of the circuit to be cleaned.

Many CIP installations are now permanently equipped with in-line temperature, rate of flow and conductivity probes which provide a recorded graph of each programme run. The daily print-out can be compared with an 'ideal' graph in order to give an early warning of plant malfunction.

CIP installations, containing interface detection, have suffered as a result of incorrect calibration and lack of maintenance. The following vicious circle of errors leads to heavy losses:

- the detergent tank high level contact is made before all the detergent is returned;
- high-concentration detergent is diverted to the water reclaim tank which is used for pre-rinsing;
- the detergent-rich reclaimed water upsets the interface detection of the following cleaning cycle (the system will switch to recirculation before the correct solution has fully charged the circuit);
- at the end of the cycle even stronger detergent solutions are diverted to the reclaim tank;
- the automatic detergent make-up comes into play during the detergent recirculation and, at the end of this part of the programme, there is again no room for all the detergent in the detergent tank and again the reclaim tank is needlessly strengthened by detergent-rich water.

Plant is available to clean up used and contaminated alkaline and acid detergents. Mechanical separation of the impurities allows the detergents to be reused over a long period of time.

In order to reduce detergent and effluent losses, mechanical separation is usually essential for caustic-based detergents used to clean plant which is handling very high fat content products.

Pesticide manufacturers in The Netherlands have reduced the amount of waste water produced during cleaning by:

- using different production lines for different kinds of products so that the number of cleaning procedures can be reduced;
- always using a dry cleaning step;
- cleaning with non-halogenated organic solvents instead of water (the solvent can be reused after reclamation with activated carbon);
- using high pressure (for the shortest possible time) when water is necessary for cleaning, thus creating less waste water.

SOFTENED WATER

The white deposit that forms in domestic kettles is evidence of hard water. What is inside is the temporary hardness — temporary because it deposits out on heating. The rate of deposit increases gradually as the temperature increases (see Figure 5.4). Hardness is mainly attributable to salts picked up by soft rainwater passing over and through rock which releases calcium and magnesium into the water. In very hard rock areas, such as Scotland, the rock is not dissolved and so naturally soft water results . Soft acidic water flows from peat moors.

For convenience, laboratory test results for hardness are expressed as calcium carbonate ($CaCO_3$) in milligrams per litre. Descriptions of relative total hardness are shown in Table 5.1. The most common softening process used by industry and commerce is ion exchange in which calcium and magnesium ions, which cause hardness, are exchanged for sodium ions. Small resin beads within the softener provide the surface area over which the exchange takes place.

TABLE 5.1
Description of levels of total hardness

Level	mg per litre calcium carbonate ($CaCO_3$)
Soft	0–50
Moderately soft	50–100
Slightly hard	100–150
Moderately hard	150–200
Hard	200–300
Very hard	>300

Water usage by ion exchange softeners is influenced by, amongst other things:

- salt quantity per unit volume of resin;
- the salt concentration used to regenerate the resin bed. Waste water discharged during brining can vary threefold between maximum and minimum acceptable brine concentrations;
- mains water pressure;
- resin bead particle size. The smaller the beads, the quicker the rinse time during regeneration.

Most naturally soft waters are derived from upland and moorland areas and usually have a pH value of 6 or less. Their total hardness seldom exceeds 20 mg per litre. These waters are generally corrosive to most of the common

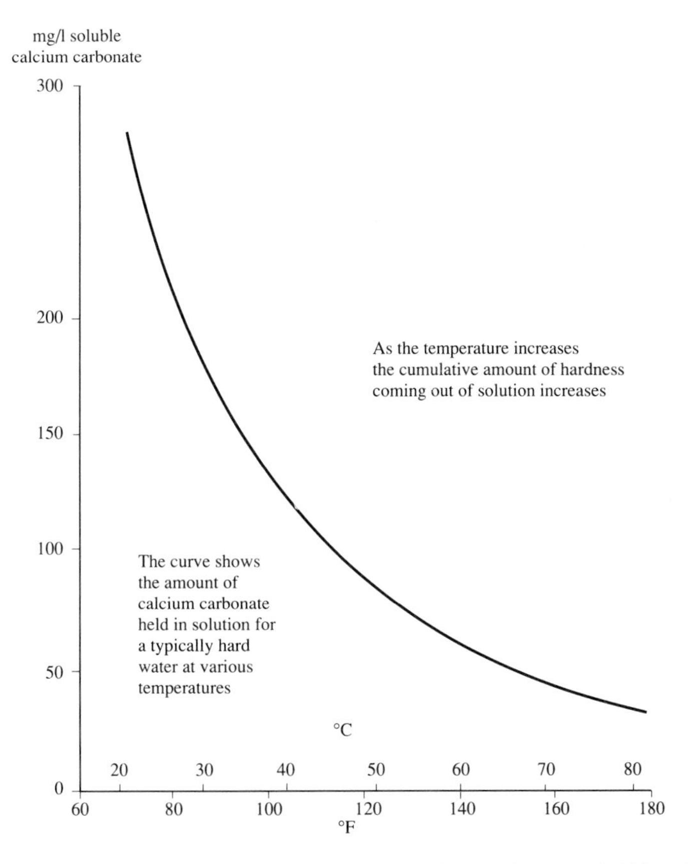

Figure 5.4 The effect of temperature on calcium carbonate solubility. (Source: Houseman (Burnham) Ltd.)

metals. Soft waters of natural origin also contain organic materials, particularly acids, which can increase the corrosion effect on materials such as copper.

A milk evaporator was cleaned, by recirculation, using moderately hard water (200 mg per litre $CaCO_3$). In a short time, the normal evaporation process had concentrated the water to a level in excess of 1000 mg per litre $CaCO_3$. This caused rapid soiling of the plant and a reduced heat transfer which were serious and costly.

MANUFACTURING — CLEANER TECHNOLOGY

For those who have the manoeuvrability, the capital and a suitable site, investing in cleaner technology can be cheaper than end-of-pipe solutions. Efficiency, raw material conservation and quality improvements are rewards for choosing this option in which, as far as possible, water use and effluent production are designed out at source.

Cleaner technology includes dealing with waste generation at source and minimizing the demand for raw materials and energy. A definition[12] used by the International Association for Clean Technology, a voluntary organization based in The Netherlands, is:

'Any environmental measure that is taken to contribute to the closure of the production-product life cycle. This could include the better use of raw materials, new processes, process integrated recycling, new product specifications and recycling of waste products as raw materials'.

Environment Business[13] reported in March 1991 that the owners of a Danish dye-works had spent nearly 40% more on a cleaner production process than they would have had to spend on a larger effluent treatment plant. Their rewards have been a near 90% cut in water consumption and a 25% cut in energy consumption, whilst production has been doubled and the fabric retention of dye has increased from 60–70% to 98%.

Another Danish company, which manufactures textiles, has implemented cleaner production in both its manufacturing processes and its products[14]. Although customers may be willing to pay for a 'green' product or service, their understanding of the degree of environmental friendliness is difficult to establish. The company has created an 'environmental scale'. Using the scale, their customers can make an intelligent choice. All products have an environmental value between 0 and 100. A value of 0 could be applied to, for instance, a nuclear bomb. A score of 100 is impossible to reach since transport, or the slightest manufacturing process, will have a negative impact on the environment.

Recovery of beer from the bottom of maturation tanks offers scope for reclaiming raw materials and reducing water consumption. During conditioning, a large amount of protein and yeast sediment settles out in ageing tanks. This bottom layer is often discarded on the final filtration of the beer prior to packaging, typically contributing 5% to the effluent load. The installation of filters which can handle the high solids content of this waste shows a rapid payback as it:

- recovers beer which can be reprocessed;
- removes solids, reducing pollution load;
- opens up the opportunity for the solids to be sold as animal feed.

The weak wort (the 'last runnings') produced in the final stages of the lauter tun (mash separator) run-off, could be used in the next mash and not disposed of to drain. In the UK, excise duty is no longer payable immediately prior to fermentation. The 'duty point' is usually when the product leaves the factory gate. If management applies an accounting duty point at the sewer, this adds value to product losses and makes it more attractive to prevent such losses.

Advances in leather technology have allowed 9% chromium, instead of the normal 17%, to be used in the tanning process. Residual chrome in the spent liquor is reduced because less is used in the process and also because the technique increases the percentage uptake in the hides. Other cleaner technologies, reported by the British Leather Federation[15] as being introduced into the leather industry, include:

- hide chilling to avoid salt in the effluent;
- hair recovery processes to reduce BOD and COD of the effluent;
- enzyme-assisted unhairing to reduce sulphide;
- deliming with carbon dioxide to reduce ammonia in the environment and effluent.

Wool destined for use in high quality carpets contains up to 10% grease, together with dust and other contaminants. The traditional washing process produces a potent waste stream which attracts high costs for disposal to sewer. The introduction, at a Kidderminster factory, of an ultrafiltration unit has enabled a reduction in the COD and suspended solids discharged to sewer. The concentrated stream, not discharged to sewer, is rich in potassium and nitrogen and is used on local grassland. The capital investment resulted in a 20 month payback.

The textile dyeing and finishing industry in The Netherlands has applied the following process changes, to reduce the amount of persistent dyes and toxic finishers discharged to sewer:

- the use of peroxide instead of chlorine in the bleaching process to avoid the formation of chlorinated compounds;
- avoiding the need for chlorinated carriers used in combination with certain dyes, by replacing them with non-halogenated compounds;

• producing only the amount of dye needed, by automated dye preparation, thereby minimizing waste;
• rinsing the excess dye for reuse (if no reuse is expected, a mixture of left-overs can be used for black colours);
• selecting the most environmentally harmful of the large number of chemicals used in the processes (in terms of toxicity, persistence, etc) and replacing them with less harmful alternatives.

The next step beyond cleaner technology could be the concept of 'zero emissions' which, although unlikely to be enshrined in legislation, has been adopted by some companies as a long-term target.

WASHING SENSITIVE PRODUCTS

If a product is sensitive to water quality, then it follows that the water treatment plant operation should be checked at appropriate intervals. A system should be created to check that maintenance and inspection are carried out. An example is bacterial contamination control by ultraviolet (UV) light, which is sometimes used as a final safeguard treatment on de-chlorinated water.

In order for UV light to do the job required of it — namely to penetrate through to the micro-organisms for long enough and in a large enough dose to kill them — it is necessary to ensure that the optimum conditions exist. This requires regular maintenance of the apparently simple equipment and regular testing of the water quality. Factors which affect the operation (and presumably profits) include:
• deterioration in the quality of the water being presented to the device. This can be detected by a monitor and alarm;
• an increase in water velocity through the sterilizer, thus reducing the residence time and the sterilizing effect. A flow control device can be fitted;
• a deposit on the UV-transparent quartz sleeve over which the water flows, thus reducing the destruction of micro-organisms. The monitor should signal that the quartz sleeve needs cleaning;
• the effective life of the artificial UV radiation source. Lamps need replacement and monitors need calibration.

USE OF WATER AS SUPPLIED

'As supplied' is probably the largest proportion of water use and the most diverse throughout industry. Here some of the measures which have been taken to reduce consumption are mentioned.

USE IN THE PRODUCT

If water is untreated before use, any variability in the quality of the water as supplied could affect the quality of the product. Because the user does not control mains water quality, monitoring is an important responsibility. Water that is perfectly wholesome to drink may not always be suitable for the product.

If water is used in a product which is destined for human consumption, then the public must be protected. Quality assurance personnel and the local authority Environmental Health Officers should ensure that correct standards are maintained. It may be possible to improve the competitiveness of the product by improving the quality of the water. The level of sub-standard product or customer complaints might be reduced if the water treatment process were upgraded. This is particularly the case if, for example, the water is de-chlorinated in order to protect a product whose taste would be harmed by the presence of chlorine. The subsequent handling of the unprotected de-chlorinated water will be one of the weak points in the process.

Whilst gas and electricity are sold to tight quality standards, water supply quality — although now required to be within set limits — can vary enormously in chemical content, with consequent repercussions in the process. The quality of the water used may well be of the utmost importance for the production process and it would seem reasonable to be alert to risks and problems. Seek the best advice possible, at the earliest opportunity, to ensure that the water supply is being handled correctly.

WASHING THE PRODUCT

Product washing allows, in some cases, for the flow of water to go in the opposite direction to the product and for the water to be reused for pre-rinsing. So, the cleanest water washes the nearly clean product and the reused water washes the dirty incoming product. This counter-current technique saves not only water, but also effluent volume. The effluent may be more concentrated and easier to clean, or may even allow product or by-product recovery.

If the product flow-line is subject to stoppages, it is worthwhile fitting automatic cut-off valves on the water line. Start-up of the process may need to have a built-in delay following reactivation of the water flow. Quality control is important.

Standfast Dyers and Printers Ltd in Lancaster invested in modern counter-current plant with subsequent benefits to its water and, particularly, its trade effluent costs. Traditionally, cloth was prepared for printing by heating and bleaching in a batch tank. After each batch the contaminated liquor was discharged to drain. Through capital investment in modern counter-flow plant, in which the process water is filtered to remove sediment and reused in the process, a 70% saving on energy and on water and effluent volumes has been made. Although the reduced volume has meant that pH neutralization is now required, this is an insignificant cost to set against the substantial monetary savings which have been achieved[16].

Spent rinse water used in the microelectronics industry is usually only slightly contaminated and very often of better quality than the raw water supplied to the plant. At one factory, a treatment plant paid for itself in 18 months. Spent rinse waters are fed to a recirculation tank, and from there organic contaminants are removed by an activated carbon filter before the water is deionized and returned to the product rinse tank to be used again.

When highly toxic materials are being rinsed, a reclaim loop could be incorporated in the water treatment plant. When deionization equipment is part of the process, waste products are obtained in concentrated form during the regeneration process. Concentrated effluents can be treated more cost effectively and precious metals may be recovered more easily.

TRANSPORTING THE PRODUCT

A number of measures can be considered where water is used to transport product. Is it possible to recycle the water? Is water the only vehicle? By how much would the cost of water have to increase before an alternative transport method becomes more attractive?

COOKING THE PRODUCT

Is the process continuous or batch? If batch, are the heat and water at least partially recoverable and reusable within the cooking process or elsewhere in the factory? Are the controls and sensors giving accurate information and is excess heat or water being reused? If one large volume of product has to be heated or cooled by water, it may be possible to carry out the task more economically by allowing an intermittent flow of water. Heat transfer can be lengthy, and stopping the water flow provides the time for the optimum of heat to transfer to or from the product. The reduction in water use can be substantial.

MAKING UP DETERGENTS

If the water supply is hard, it should be cheaper and more efficient to use softened water (see page 81).

PRE-WASHING AND FINAL RINSING OF CONTAINERS

Many industries have reusable containers that hold product. Milk bottles are a good example. Milk crates are also washed and reused.

Some of the features of bottle washers and the principles and lessons learned from their operation are worth noting as they are relevant to many other items of water-using plant.

The bottles passing through the washer are rinsed, cleaned with hot detergent and then rinsed with clean water (see Figure 5.5). The pipes in the washer are arranged so as to enable final rinse water to be reused for pre-rinse and for the hot detergent to be recycled. Provided that the washer design is suitable, it is important to ensure that the water being used is soft. Some types of bottle washer encourage the foaming (fobbing) of detergent solutions which, in turn, creates increased effluent losses.

The rate of flow to the washer should be as specified by the manufacturer and metered and controlled by a rate-of-flow indicator; attention to this one item alone can save significant sums on water and effluent accounts. If no rate-of-flow indicator is fitted, the flow of water through the washing jets may be affected by fluctuations in the pressure of water feeding the washer. This pressure could be controlled by a pressure regulating valve, a break tank or a rate-of-flow controller. The flow balance through the washer should also be checked regularly. Any overflow at the discharge end is an unnecessary waste.

The addition of detergent must be controlled and sensed with instrumentation that works. This is especially necessary to save detergent, but also to keep within trade effluent consent limits or to avoid 'knocking out' an on-site effluent treatment plant. Figure 5.6 shows, in the case of a caustic-based detergent, what can happen if control is lax.

The hot vapours from the washer must be discharged to atmosphere. In a controlled way, and with the knowledge of the manufacturer, it may be possible to reduce the vapour and thus the heat loss by restricting the flow

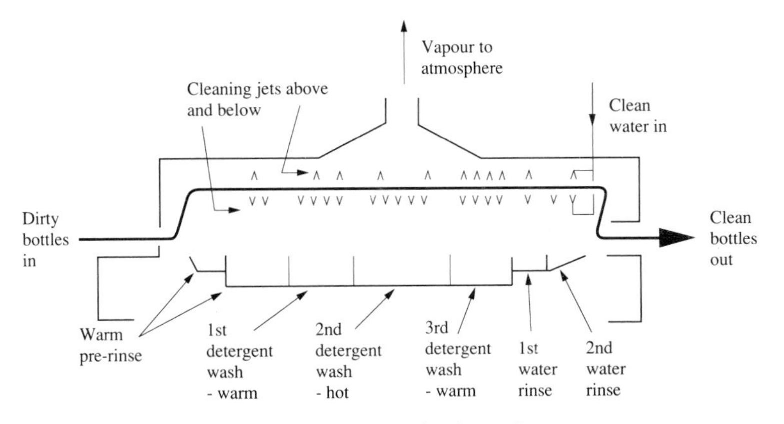

Figure 5.5 Straight-through sprayer type bottle washer.

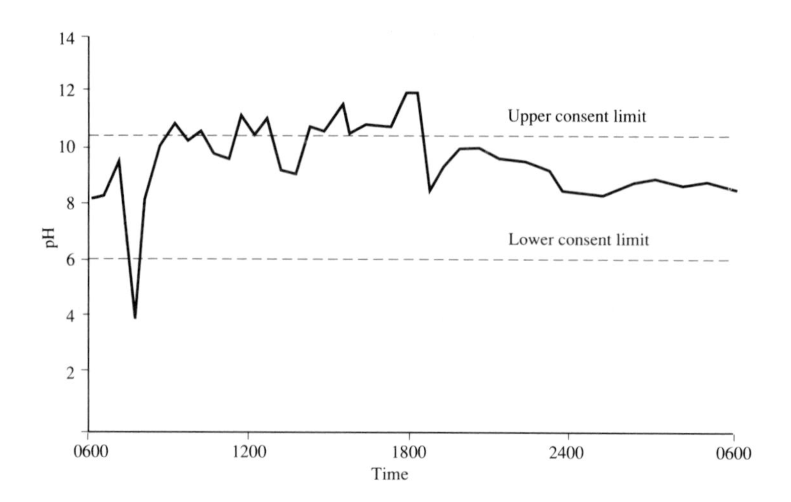

Figure 5.6 Unsatisfactory pH variation in a trade effluent discharge containing caustic-based detergents.

through the discharge duct. No condensation should be allowed to appear on the bottle however, nor drips to enter the cleaned bottle.

A check can be made to see if all the jets in the washer are needed to deal with the cleaning job presented to them. Fewer jets in use means less water usage. Regular checks to see that the jet openings are correct and not enlarged through erosion will help ensure that minimum water usage is maintained.

Correct hot water and detergent temperatures are important. Are the gauges accurately calibrated? Due to better detergent formulation and the provision of less overkill, washing temperatures have been reduced over recent years.

When washing reusable containers, some unused product may remain in the container. The easy but wrong way of dealing with this is to let it go through the washer, pushing up effluent disposal costs at the same time. The correct way is to ensure that the excess is collected in a container and disposed of separately, either to a waste-tip or, if the substance is suitable, for animal feed. Work done over 20 years ago[17], on the draining of ten-gallon milk churns, amply illustrates the need for an adequate draining time to be built into the design of any tipping apparatus (see Figure 5.7). Milk is a potent polluter.

For neatness, discharges to drain are sealed from view. Although the effect will not be as visually pleasing, it is well worth arranging discharges so that the strength of the effluent as well as the rate of flow can be seen. The other important advantage is that the discharge can be sampled as part of an investigation (see Chapter 7) or as part of regular checks on plant efficiency.

It may be possible for suitable detergent overflows from the main washer to be reused in the crate washer, thereby saving water, heat, detergent and effluent costs. Final rinse sprays can be fed from reclaimed water. Allowing faulty crates or those containing rubbish to enter the washer causes jams and wastage. An arrangement should allow suspect crates to be removed from the conveyer prior to entering the washer and consideration could be given to installing crate turners to tip out rubbish automatically. If the multi-trip crates are damaged but usable, submerging them in an ultrasonic cleaning tank may be preferable. The tank can be fed with recycled water via a mechanical sludge separator. This saves water and effluent and produces an acceptable finished article.

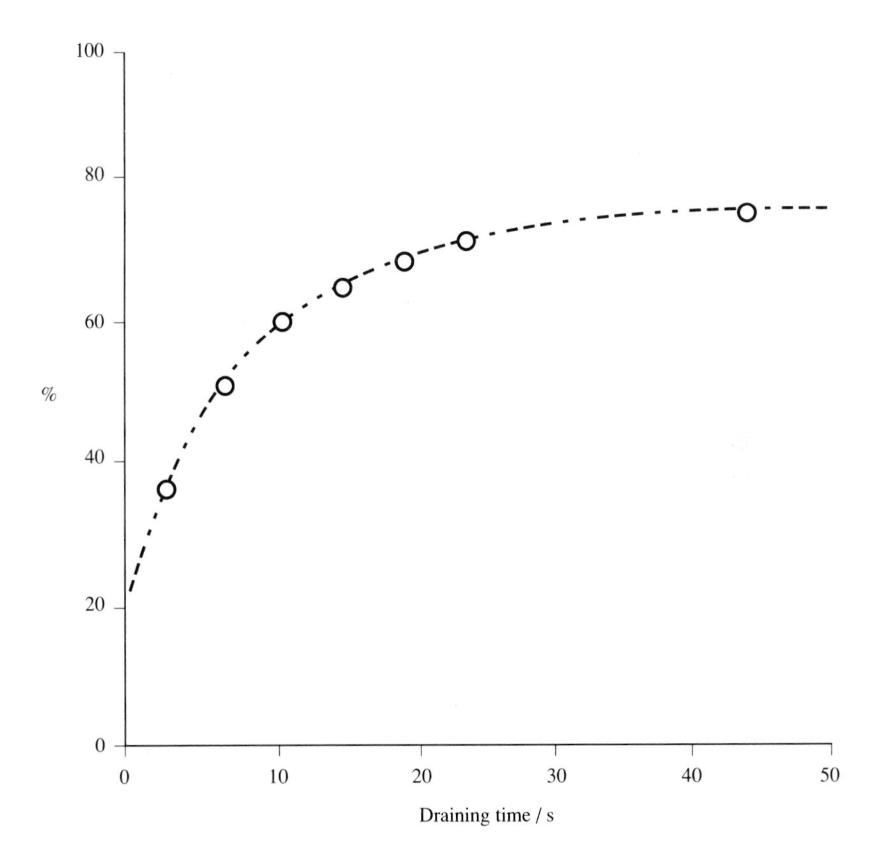

Figure 5.7 Relationship between draining time and percentage of remaining milk recovered from properly dumped cans. (Source: Agriculture and Food Development Authority, Dublin.)

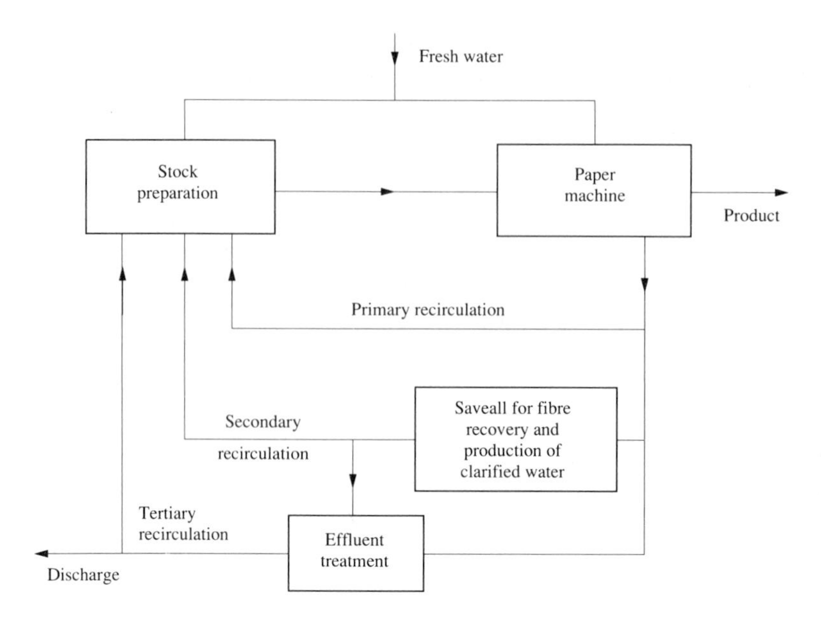

Figure 5.8 Water recirculation circuits in paper/board making. (Source: PIRA, Leatherhead.)

On a few sites, and with varying degrees of success, the effluent from a bottle washer has been segregated, passed to an on-site treatment plant and then recycled as the main supply to the washer. Obviously, this closing-the-loop activity needs to be undertaken with care. Constantly recycling water, in which contaminants and detergents are mixed with the original clean water, results in a build-up of dissolved solids in the water. A point is reached where fresh make-up water is needed to keep the dissolved solids at an acceptable level. To achieve a dilution and at the same time protect the quality of the washed container, the final row of washing jets can be fed from a fresh, not recycled, water supply.

When considering tailor-made treatment plant to handle and recycle the effluent from equipment such as a bottle washer, there may be little difficulty in justifying the expenditure. For example, if a production site is to be expanded, but there are physical restrictions on the water supply or effluent disposal flows, then recycling could be the answer. Where no such restrictions exist, then the overall economics will need to be assessed in terms of:

- value of the site space required for the treatment plant;
- the possibility of heat recovery;
- staff required to look after plant;

- the ability to maintain the required treated water quality;
- the water and effluent cost savings which will help pay for the plant (see also 'Recycling Treated Effluent' (page 96) and Figure 5.8 which shows recycling in the paper and board industry).

Significant savings can be made on bottlewashing and other water-using plant when, as always happens, the washing operation is interrupted for rest periods or because of a fault. When the plant stops, a signal should be sent to an automatic shut-off valve to stop the flow of water. Obviously, this has to be done carefully to ensure that machinery does not run dry and that, on start-up, no items emerge in an unwashed condition.

Corning Process Systems in Staffordshire provides equipment to handle the rinse waters from chrome and nickel electroplating drag-out tanks. The waters are heavily laden with expensive chemicals which present high-cost disposal problems. The plating chemicals can be removed and returned to the plating bath at bath concentration. The remaining water can be returned to the wash tanks. Over 90% chemical recovery can be achieved.

HEATING

Water is often used as the vehicle to carry heat through a factory or a process. Pay attention to the quality of the water. Softening prevents the deposit of scale, whilst corrosion can be avoided by careful pre-treatment, selection of the materials of construction for the heating system, or chemical additives. Heat escape can be prevented by lagging or by stopping leaks. There may also be an opportunity on the site for upgrading heat by means of a heat pump.

The Shirley Institute[18] (now Shirley Technology Centre within BTTG) has been highlighting water savings as part of energy management investigations for members and clients. One survey at a bleaching company found:

- heated water, some relatively uncontaminated, was being discharged to drain when it could be reused in the dirtiest washing stage of the process. (A temperature recording of the flow of effluent from a site is most revealing and is more than likely to highlight potential savings);
- improvements could be made to lagging of hot water lines;
- the ultimate effluent discharge could be put through a heat-exchanger in order to transfer the heat to the incoming cold fresh water supply.

The result was a saving of nearly 10% in the total energy requirement for that production site. Further investigation led to:

- the use of foam to reduce water used in a padding and drying operation from 65 to 30% of the fabric weight;

- a change in the process for preparation of fabrics to enable the preparation sequence to be carried out with cold instead of hot water;
- the reduction of the volume discharged to waste which in turn cut effluent costs by 13%.

Another Shirley Institute energy investigation at a textile printing company has shown the cost advantages to be gained from self-contained direct steam or hot water generation at the various points of use within a process. The inference is that in some industrial works it may well be possible to operate without a boilerhouse. The ability to produce hot water on demand only eliminates the need for storage vessels and their attendant heat losses.

Water-borne waste heat from the pasteurizing process associated with a beer bottling line is used to heat the packaging hall in winter.

An article in *Warmer Bulletin*[19] reported on collaboration between South Western Electricity (SWE) and the National Shire Horse Centre, where a vertical radiator was installed in a chute fed with manure. The manure decays over an eight-week period and is sold as a growing medium. SWE has estimated that the maturing manure is capable of saving the Centre up to £10,000 a year on heating bills for the stables, restaurant, museum, smithy and education centre. Perhaps we should go back to the horse and cart!

ONCE-THROUGH COOLING

The use of water as a cooling medium without recycle is called once-through cooling. Heat is transferred to the water via a process heat exchanger, and the water is then discharged. Assuming that the receiving water can accept a higher temperature, the economics are linked to the capital and volumetric cost of the cooling water and its availability.

Water quality control in this instance is normally minimized, although care has to be taken over the correct choice of heat exchanger and the materials of construction. Cooling towers have replaced many once-through systems. Powergen found at its Killingholme gas-fired station that using a bank of low-level forced draught cooling towers allowed use of 25 times less water than a direct cooled power station. But, due to the use of the energy intensive fans, the overall thermal efficiency was about 50% instead of 55% with once-through cooling.

Due to the warm conditions inside a heat exchanger, deposits can occur on the heating surfaces. The surfaces need to be inspected and, if necessary, cleaned from time to time.

If the source of water is a river, or other supply which can contain debris, then attention needs to be given to protecting the water intake by screens or similar devices.

EVAPORATIVE COOLING

The principle of cooling by evaporation to dissipate heat from the circuit is applied both to the large natural draught concrete cooling towers — associated with power stations and large industrial complexes — and to the mechanical draught cooling towers incorporating fans which serve air conditioning and other installations. The hot recirculated water is discharged on to a packing medium within the tower which either films the water or converts it into droplets. Heat is transferred to the passing air by the difference in vapour pressure between the water and the colder, drier air.

One UK brewery installed a recirculating cooling system and reduced its chargeable effluent volume by 60%.

Water costs can be greatly reduced by the correct selection of tower design. Economic operation is influenced by packing selection, varying water quality, suitable water treatment and fan design and running time.

The evaporative water loss through such a system is approximately 1% of the circulating flow for each 5.5°C drop in temperature. Any additional loss from drift carryover or from spray at the air inlets can and should be limited to 0.1% of the circulating flow. Thus, if the circulating water flow is 100 cubic metres per hour (22,000 gph) and the tower cools the water from 37.7°C down to 24°C, the evaporative loss would be about 2.5% plus 0.1% for carryover. The total make-up required should be about 2.6 cubic metres per hour (570 gph). Depending on the quality of the make-up water, and the surrounding atmosphere, there will also be a wastage to drain in order to keep the dissolved and suspended solids at an acceptable level. It may be worth installing a filter system, to remove dirt, dust, slime and dead algae which not only reduce the cooling circuit's efficiency but also provide part of the special conditions needed for the multiplication of *Legionella pneumophilia*.

Many cooling tower owners may be unaware of the theoretical amount of make-up which is needed. For many towers (and many items of water-using plant) it is relatively cheap and easy to fit a water meter to the make-up pipeline in order to keep a check on the efficiency of the tower (see Figure 4.1 on page 66). The packing inside towers can become blocked, or deteriorate. How many times has the make-up to towers been augmented by a hosepipe! That is surely a sign of the need for an investigation to find out why the extra make-up is needed.

The make-up water required for cooling towers is a prime candidate for reusing waste streams from other processes, providing a suitable source and quality of waste water can be found on site. The almost hidden advantage is that there is no cost attaching to the disposal of the reused water as it is evaporated into the atmosphere. Any proposal should be discussed with the tower manufacturer.

The marine mussel is kept under control in power station cooling water circuits by chlorination. At some sites, a small barrel-shaped container has been incorporated in a bypass in order to signal the appearance of mussel spat. At a study site, chlorination was started when the seawater temperature rose above 10°C. With the help of the monitor, chlorination was delayed until the spat were seen to settle, resulting in a 30% reduction in hypochlorite consumption. The monitor can be used to test the effectiveness of additives and coatings[20].

Finally, is it really necessary to use water? A number of small cooling duties, which do not require the lower wet bulb temperatures achieved by water cooling towers, can be performed satisfactorily and economically by using air cooling.

FLOOR AND YARD WASHING

Where product is spilt, or fragments drop to the floor, it is not always necessary to use water to clean up. If the floors cannot be brushed clean — and this should be done to remove solids before hosing down anyway — then the use of industrial floor cleaners should be considered. If liquid product is spilt, this can be removed by the use of suitable industrial vacuum cleaners that can handle liquids.

A CBI publication[21] quotes the example of Bluecrest Convenience Foods Ltd, which is saving £60,000 per year as a result of encouraging staff not to sweep waste food scraps down the drain and by the improved control on the dilution of cleaning fluids.

If the use of hoses is unavoidable, then the minimum requirement for the site should be assessed. Is cleaning best achieved with high flow and low pressure, or perhaps the opposite? Jet cleaning could be the answer. If the pressure is important, reduce the bore of the hose, and the number of hose points to a minimum and, providing steam is not used, fit a suitable hand gun at the end of the hose so the flow ceases as soon as the operator lets go of the hose or releases the trigger.

A brewery uses buckets of water, instead of a hose, to wash down filling machines.

Suitable quality reusable waste streams should be diverted to feed the washdown system, as this is an excellent means of saving water and energy costs.

Very often yard drains discharge to a soakaway or to a watercourse. If there is any chance of product getting into such a drain, then the drain should be connected to the foul drainage system on the site. Consider providing an overhead cover for stocks of potentially polluting raw materials and products held in the open air. Storage units and pallets for holding metal drums containing liquid are available with in-built sumps to catch spillages and leaks.

FIRE-FIGHTING

Water for fire-fighting when taken from the mains supply should be free of charge. Charges are levied for the installation of fire hydrants and to cover other benefits of a separate fire main. If there are a number of fire hose points on site, check to see if any are fed through a meter. A rebate should be obtainable for any metered water used to fight a fire. Whether fed through a meter or not, it is wise to ensure that fire hoses are not used for other purposes, unless as part of a periodic check on their correct operation.

LEISURE

Modern enclosed multi-pool leisure complexes create both challenges and problems for the designer and plant supplier. In order to continue to attract the public, new water-related features are often added or installed to replace existing features that are less popular. The warm pool water and warm air over the pool, both of which are recycled, give opportunities for the use of heat exchangers and heat pumps. However, the recycling and warmth also provide the ideal environment for unwanted bacteria growth. The Sports Council and others[22,23] are able to supply information and literature on this subject.

GARDENS

Staff working at commercial and industrial sites, and the general public, enjoy the amenity provided by lawns, flower beds and potted plants. A Thames Water leaflet, *Watering your Garden — the Good Kew Guide*, gives many examples of how the Royal Botanic Gardens, Kew, advises gardeners to save water. Lawns benefit from infrequent but thorough watering. Sprinklers should be moved about to ensure even watering. On average, a sprinkler uses in one hour as much water as a family of four uses in two days. Mulching helps conserve soil moisture.

RECYCLING TREATED EFFLUENT

The recycle of treated effluent is not at all uncommon. In dry countries, municipalities are reusing effluent for purposes other than drinking, and a few even for drinking. Work was done in the food industry in the 1960s to prove that the loop could be closed on a site which had its own river water treatment plant and effluent treatment plant. It is likely that if standards tighten and charges for direct discharges to watercourses and water abstraction increase, the reuse of effluent will take place on many sites. The recent development of cross-flow microfiltration should make the reuse of suitable waste streams more feasible.

A company and a research institute in Japan have developed a system for treating complex cyanide in waste water from a plating factory[24]. Ultraviolet light and ozone degrade the complexes without the need for chemicals. The metal oxides and undissolved cyanide are then filtered out leaving an ion exchange system to remove ions in the treated solution, thus purifying the waste water for recycling.

Process plant is available for treating laundry effluent and returning up to 85% for reuse. Temperature losses between the effluent and the returned water are minimized to about 7–10°C. The plant uses a combination of chemicals, flotation and sand filtration. Capital payback is said to be achieved in just under three years on suitable sites.

Paper and board-making processes require large quantities of good quality water[24]. Figure 5.8 (see page 91) shows that it is possible to have three recirculation loops. Note that the tertiary loop involves the effluent treatment plant. In June 1985 the average process water consumption at UK paper mills was about 40 cubic metres per tonne. With the sort of recycling shown in Figure 5.8, consumption can be cut by three quarters to ten cubic metres per tonne or less. Electrodialysis has been used as a technique for the recovery of sulphite and for de-salting dyes, as part of the recycling process. A Swedish consultancy firm conducted an environmental impact study for a Malaysian pulp and paper mill. Amongst the design features incorporated were the following:

- dry barking of logs;
- short sequence three-stage pulp bleaching to reduce pollution load;
- installation of a highly efficient chemical recovery boiler;
- reburning of lime mud in a lime kiln;
- use of membrane technology for the production of chlorine and sodium hydroxide free from mercury and asbestos pollution;
- an integrated chlorine dioxide process which eliminates the need to dispose of spent acid;
- a spill control system to control accidental discharges;
- closed loop water recirculation in the mill to reduce the quantity of effluent.

Work has been carried out in the textile industry on using treated municipal sewage effluent from a water utility works[26]. It was felt that significant reductions in demand for top quality water could be realized by accepting lower grade water for non-critical processes. The potential reduction of running costs and overheads as a result of recycling trade effluents could be of great benefit to the UK textile industry. Surely the textile industry is not unique in this respect. Permanent space stations will require a totally enclosed environment and water (which costs about £4.50 per litre to deliver into space) will have to be used over and over again.

SOURCES OF INFORMATION

REFERENCES IN CHAPTER 5

1. Compagnie Vaudoise d' Electricité, 34 Avenue du Tribunal-Federal, 1000 Lausanne, Switzerland.
2. *Chlorination of Drinking Water. A Short Guide to Process Design*, 1990 (British Water).
3. *Proceedings of IDF Seminar on Dairy Effluents. Document 184*, 1984 (International Dairy Federation).
4. *Legionella — A BEWA Guide*, 1993 (British Water). A free A4 6-page leaflet which includes a list of additional sources of information.
5. *The Notification of Cooling Towers and Evaporative Condensers Regulations 1992 (SI 1992 No 2225)* (HMSO).
6. Legionnaire's Disease — The Implications for Design and Use of Hot Water Systems, *Information Paper IP 5/85* (Building Research Establishment).
7. British Pump Manufacturer's Association (BPMA), 8th Floor, Bridge House, 121 Smallbrook, Queensway, Birmingham B5 4JP, tel: 0121 643 3377, fax: 0121 643 5064. The trade association of liquid pump manufacturers.
8. Choosing a better steam trap, *The Plant Engineer*, 1994, 38 (1): 14–15.
9. *The Energy Saver* (Gee Publishing).
10. *The Urban Waste Water Treatment (England and Wales) Regulations 1994 (SI 1994 No 2841)* (HMSO).
11. *The Urban Waste Water Treatment (Scotland) Regulations 1994 (SI 1994 No 2842 (S.144)* (HMSO).
12. Advisory Council on Science and Technology (ACOST), 1992, *Cleaner Technology* (HMSO).
13. Cleaner plant reaps big rewards in Denmark, *Environment Business*, 13 March 1991, 6.
14. Novotex and 'green cotton': an example of cleaner production in the textile industry, *Cleaner Production*, No 6 Spring 1993. (The newsletter of UNEP IE/PAC.)
15. Corning, D.R. and Sykes, R.L. (British Leather Foundation), 1990, Waste management in the tanning industry, *Industrial Waste Management*, December 1990, 11.
16. Sharratt, P.N., 1993, *Waste minimisation for batchwise extraction processes, in Effluent Treatment and Waste Minimisation, IChemE Symposium Series No 132* (IChemE).
17. *Reduction of Pollution due to Milk Losses in the Dairy Industry*, 1971 (Agriculture and Food Development Authority (Teagasc), Ireland).
18. Shirley Technology Centre, Shirley Towers, Wilmslow Road, Didsbury, Manchester M20 8RY, tel: 0161 445 8141, fax: 0161 434 9957. Was formerly the Shirley Institute, now known as the Shirley Technology Centre, part of the British Textile Technology Group (BTTG)
19. Horse power with a difference, *Warmer Bulletin (World Action for Recycling Materials and Energy from Rubbish)*, November 1993 No 39, 8.

20. Jenner, H.A., 1983, *A Microcosm Monitoring Mussel Fouling* (N V KEMA (Joint Laboratory and Consulting Services of the Dutch Electricity Supply Companies), PO Box 9035, 6800 ET Arnhem, The Netherlands).
21. *Environment Costs. The Effects on Competitiveness of the Environment, Health and Safety*, 1994 (Confederation of British Industry).
22. Pool Water Treatment Advisory Group, Field House, Thrandeston, Near Diss, Norfolk IP21 4BU.
23. The Sports Council, 16 Upper Woburn Place, London WC1H 0QP.
24. Plating waste water treatment and recycling system, *New Technology Japan, March 1993* (Japan External Trade Organization, Machinery and Technology Dept., 2–5, Toranomon 2-chome, Minato-ku, Tokyo 105, Japan), 39.
25. PIRA, Randalls Road, Leatherhead, Surrey KT22 7RU. The research association for the paper, board, printing and packaging industries.
26. *The Pudsey Project — The Recycling of Treated Sewage Effluent for Use in Textile Wet Processing, WIRA Report 291*, 1981 (WIRA Technology Group (formerly the Wool Industry Research Association and now part of the British Textile Technology Group)).

FURTHER HELP AND ADVICE

DTI Environmental Management Options Scheme (DEMOS), Department of Trade and Industry, Environment Unit, 151 Buckingham Palace Road, London SW1W 9SS. Aims to promote widespread adoption of technologies and best environmental practice among companies. Offers financial support annually on a collaborative basis.

Energy-Saving Information Exchange (CADDET), ETSU Enquiries Bureau, Energy Technical Support Unit, B 156 Harwell Laboratory, Oxfordshire OX11 0RA. Information source on commercially demonstrated technologies, supported by UK and 14 overseas governments.

International Cleaner Production Information Clearinghouse (ICPIC), Industry and Environment Office, United Nations Environment Programme, 39–43 quai André Citroën, 75739 Paris CEDEX 15, France. Promotes cleaner production free-of-charge through technology transfer, education, and public awareness. Publishes *Industry and Environment*.

Manufacturing and the Environment — An Executive Guide, 1992, (Department of Trade and Industry).

Society of Chemical Industry (SCI), 14–15 Belgrave Square, London SW1X 8PS, tel: 0171 235 3681, fax: 0171 823 1698. Organizes meetings and conferences. Works jointly with other similar societies and associations throughout Europe.

TREATassist, bHr Group Limited, Cranfield, Bedford MK43 0AJ. A service for auditing process plants in the water, chemical, pharmaceutical and food industries by taking a total systems approach.

6. SAVINGS IN THE TREATMENT OF WATER AND EFFLUENT

Specialists will say, quite correctly, of the treatment of water[1–3] and effluent[4,5] that each is a distinct subject in its own right. However, in furthering efforts to avoid unnecessary expenditure and waste in commerce and industry, it is interesting to discover the similarities in the treatment of clean and dirty waters. Incidentally, the Organization for Economic Co-operation and Development (OECD)[6] sees a 4% growth in water and effluent treatment between now and the year 2000.

A number of the comments which follow apply equally to processes used for water treatment and for effluent treatment.

INITIAL CONSIDERATIONS

IN-HOUSE TREATMENT

'Do not treat unless you have to' is an obvious starting point — unless an economic return can be achieved by material recovery, recycling or reduced charges. A systematic approach to the need, or otherwise, for wastewater treatment is set out in Figure 6.1 on page 100. Industrialists are in business to make a product — not to treat water and effluent. Water undertakers exist to carry out this function for 99% of the resident population of the UK in the case of water, and 94% in the case of sewage. The charges from the water undertakers for working on such a large scale should be cheaper than industry can achieve, but that is not always the case. It pays to keep under review the cost of in-house treatment against that of the water undertaker, assuming that a raw water supply is available to serve a water treatment plant and there is space for an on-site effluent treatment plant. Site area requirements for treatment plant can be a problem, but technical progress is now allowing more throughput from a given plan area. It is also enabling existing plants to be uprated or reduced in size.

Article 11 and Annex 1 item C of the EC urban waste water treatment directive (Chapter 5, References 10 and 11) state that:

'Industrial wastewater entering collecting systems and urban wastewater treatment plants shall be subject to such pre-treatment as is required in order to:

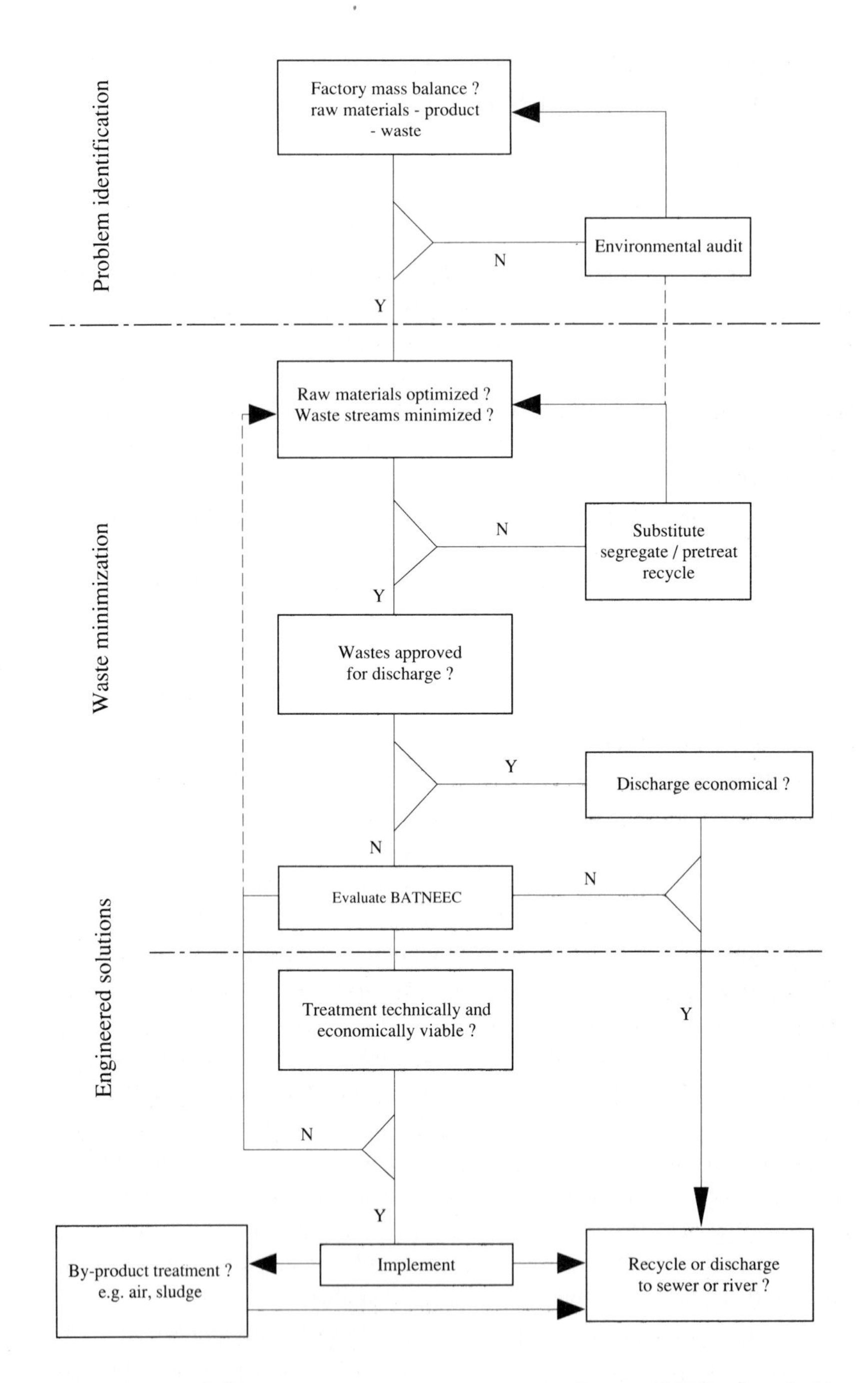

Figure 6.1 A decision route to waste water treatment. (Source: PWT Projects Ltd.)

- ensure that discharges from the treatment plants do not adversely affect the environment, or prevent receiving water from complying with other Community Directives;
- ensure that sludge can be disposed of safely in an environmentally acceptable manner.'

This effectively means that some industrial discharges to sewer will be subject to such pre-treatment as is deemed necessary by the operator of the treatment works. This could increase the discharger's costs significantly and/or bring about a renewed commitment to in-factory wastage control.

For those with plenty of space, such as British Steel Strip Products, Llanwern, it may be advantageous to plant a reed bed and let that do some of the treatment. At Llanwern, the effluent produced during cokemaking is fed into a bed of phragmites reeds where micro-organisms, which inhabit the root system, break down the contaminants into simple non-toxic compounds. The 18-acre reed bed replaces the existing treatment plant, with consequent major energy savings and a reduction in disposal costs for waste water (Chapter 5, Reference 24).

TREAT LESS

A natural result of applying the saving techniques described in Chapters 4, 5 and 8 is that less will be treated. It is reasonable to accept that the cost per unit volume will accelerate as quality standards for treated water or effluent become tighter. It is worthwhile checking on the continuing need to treat the present quantities. Log the amount treated per day and establish the cost for each cubic metre, or thousand gallons, regularly.

TREAT WELL

'Treat well' is a good rule but one that is frequently broken. Remove solids from a treatment plant intake as soon as possible before they become broken down and more expensive to treat[7]. Items of plant are often expected to do more than they were designed to achieve. This can apply to simple items, such as effluent interceptors which will not function properly unless correctly sized and, more important, emptied at the necessary intervals. On sophisticated plant, such as reverse osmosis, the need for efficient process engineering is more critical because more capital is at stake. In this case much of the cost and expertise goes into the pre-treatment — for example, by acid dosing or softening the water before it gets near the reverse osmosis membranes.

So, if treatment plant is not working properly, is it really the plant that is at fault or has it perhaps been asked to do an impossible task, or one which has become more difficult? This is why it is important for the client to prepare a concise and informative functional specification for the plant, before putting it out to tender. The client should set up appropriate consultancy and/or consultation meetings to identify and specify the duties to be performed by the treatment plant[8]. Time spent at the conceptual stage results in smoother project execution and much-reduced operational troubleshooting.

Cryptosporidia oocysts in treated water used for drinking have caused outbreaks of diarrhoea, abdominal pain, vomiting and fever. The initial message from researchers into how best to reduce the risk of the organism passing through a treatment works is that conventional filtration plant is effective in removing the organism, provided the plant is operated in accordance with good practice.

THE IMPORTANCE OF MONITORING

Plant needs to be monitored in order to ensure the production of an outflow to the standard required. Where on-site effluent treatment is installed, monitoring can also be one of the important checks on the health of a factory.

A number of simple and portable test kits are available. Instruments that are referred to as 'intelligent sensors' are now in use. These carry out calibrations and self-checks automatically and alert the operator if the performance of the instrument, or the validity of a measurement, is suspect.

Taking measurements just for the sake of it is costly; avoid doing it. It is very disheartening for people taking readings and doing tests when managers do not look at, or disregard, the results, especially when the evidence is shouting for action. Questions that should be raised include:

- does the monitoring have to be detailed and precise, or is it only a 'go'/'no go' answer which is required? If the latter, time and money can be saved;
- what happens to the results?
- who looks at them?
- who acts on them?
- who is interested in the results of the action?
- what are the consequences of no action?
- what information is really needed and why?
- is the monitoring information recorded in a form which can be investigated later, if a treatment plant operational problem emerges?

Monitoring in and out is relatively easy when checking on aspects that can be read by a meter, such as flow or electricity. If the industry is one that has a laboratory on site, it is also easy for other water or effluent characteristics to be analysed. The problem is to give sufficient priority to the measurements and this is where the check-list is useful.

What should be monitored depends on regulations, the value, size and importance of the treatment plant and the degree of seriousness to the business if the plant fails to achieve the specified duty. Control and cost savings through measurement are illustrated in the input and output diagram (Figure 6.2) and commented on in the sections which follow.

FLOWS
It is obvious that any process is affected by the quantity and quality of the flow of raw material on which the process has to work. Too little or too much flow affects the efficiency of both water and effluent plants. Although most plants have some overload capacity, as technology progresses and competition increases 'free' spare capacity will diminish. As a result, it is most important that a treatment plant is sized correctly to cover all reasonably foreseeable eventualities.

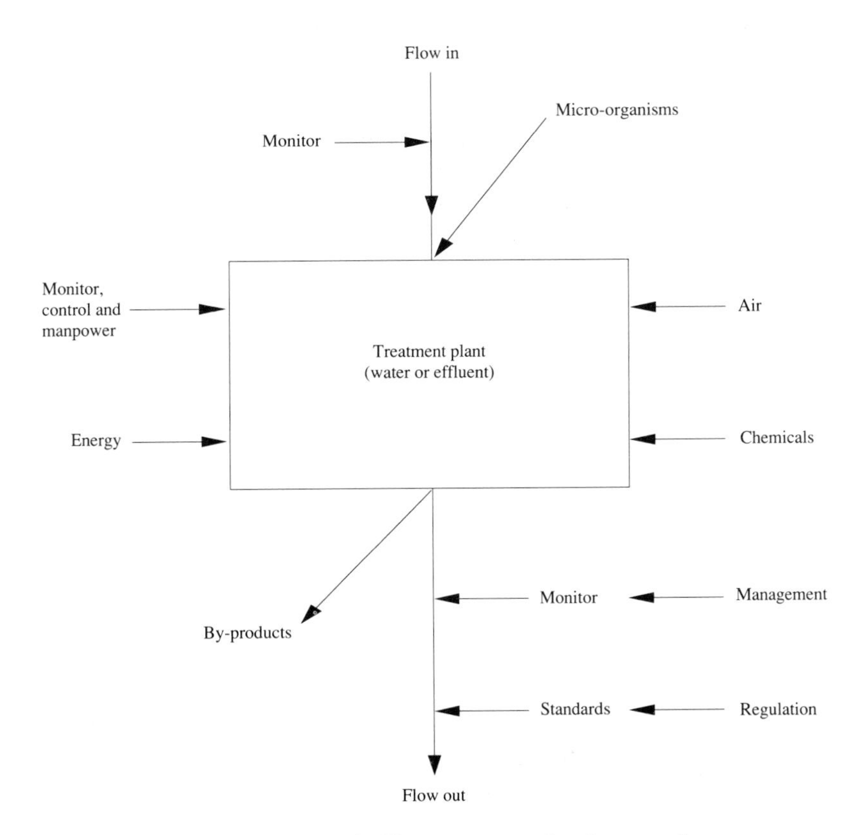

Figure 6.2 Simplified water and effluent treatment plant inputs and outputs.

The quality of the inflow is critical and what may appear easy to treat may not be so in practice. For instance, water which is described as 'thin' (usually from an upland catchment, having a reasonably clear appearance and containing less than 100 mg per litre total dissolved solids) is far more difficult to treat using conventional flocculation and settlement techniques than a muddy-looking river water. Potential suppliers of plant should be alerted to possible future needs as soon as possible, to enable water or effluent sampling to be carried out over a sufficiently long period. The quality of a natural watercourse, from which it is intended to take and treat water, changes with the seasons and also with dry and wet years. The composition of mains water also varies — quite widely in some areas. The quantity and quality of factory effluent may vary too and the swings need to be documented.

The requirements of the factory, and size and importance of an existing treatment plant, dictate the need to sample the inflow quality and measure the flow. Do not underestimate seasonal variations. One advantage of this monitoring on a water treatment plant should be the ability to take evasive action if the inflow becomes contaminated through, for instance, accidental spillage or discharge upstream.

North West Water is putting the flow from its Blackburn sewage treatment works to good use. A £600,000 expenditure on an hydroelectric turbine, placed in the outflow from the works, is to be paid back through the generator providing about 60% of the electricity needed on the treatment works.

MICRO-ORGANISMS

The water treatment process should reduce the number of bacteria and other micro-organisms in the flow[9]. In the treatment process for ultra-pure water or water used for certain medical applications, bacteria are completely eliminated.

Organically-based effluents are cleaned up using bacteria together with higher forms of life which happily inhabit the treatment process. Unless these bacteria can live in a reasonable nutrient they will not thrive; thus, things they dislike, such as high or low pH, should be avoided. More to the point, the conditions which adversely affect the bacteria may well be financially detrimental as well.

A number of companies now specialize in providing selected micro-organisms which can be introduced into effluent treatment plants to assist at the start-up of a plant, or when there is hydraulic or organic overloading. Treatment of certain difficult wastes, or problems with sludge settlement, can also be assisted. Despite the many genuine reasons for the use of such products, it is preferable to investigate and try to remove the causes of overloading, difficult wastes, sludge and other problems, as opposed to treating the effects.

The Taisei Corporation, Japan, is developing technology for manufacturing biodegradable plastics from activated sludge generated by sewage treatment[10].

TREATMENT PLANT

Because throughputs and products change in most factories, from month to month or over the years, it is inevitable that the treated quantity or quality may become out of step with the treatment plant capability. Ask the designer or supplier of the plant for advice, if there is any doubt about the ability of the plant to cope with the present circumstances. Plants installed, say, ten years ago may be good subjects for improvement or replacement. Up-rating a plant may allow some of it to be taken out of service, thereby releasing the site area for more profitable use. Treatment plant suppliers can often cure treatment plant restrictions (bottlenecks) cost effectively. There are usually a number of solutions to a water or effluent treatment problem. As a general rule, the higher the capital cost of a plant, the lower the running cost. Too often plant is purchased because it has the lowest capital cost; more weight should be given in a financial analysis to quality, reliability, operating costs and maintenance provision. Get quotations from more than one supplier.

Purac Rosewater has produced a weekly maintenance and cleaning schedule which is generated by a computer. It is claimed to take the headache out of water and waste water treatment plant operations and helps attain maximum efficiency.

The effluent, or spent wash, after the distillation of grain whisky, contains about 5% solids as a mixture of insoluble and soluble grain residues and yeast. The untreated pollution load from a distillery would be equivalent to the sewage from a largish city. Using a treatment plant, a final effluent can be produced suitable for discharge to a watercourse, together with animal feed as a by-product. Earlier effluent treatment plants employed wedge-wire screens to separate course solids, followed by multiple effect evaporators to concentrate the screened liquor, and then driers to produce the dried feeding stuff. Water removal in the drying stage is more costly than in the evaporator.

Scottish Grain Distillers replaced old effluent treatment plants with modern energy-efficient plants at two of its four large grain distilleries. The new plants use wedge-wire screens and centrifuges before more efficient evaporators. This results in the feed to the dryer having a 40%, instead of the previous 25%, dry-matter content and a consequent halving of the drying load. The annual cost of evaporation energy in such a plant was reduced from £1.27 million to £150,000 and the drying energy cost from £790,000 to £260,000. Based on a

5000-hour year, the payback on capital employed was three to four years. The most recent effluent plant also incorporates a combined heat and power system.

A review by Cremer and Warner of the industrial sectors identified in the EC urban waste water treatment directive showed that, due to the efficiency of presently available technology, 50% of the solids in a typical industrial sector effluent can be removed with ease[11].

A visual indication of the relative size of particles that can be removed by filtration[12] is given in Figure 6.3.

Bremer Woll-Kämmerei AG, Germany, has developed a process for treating heavily polluted effluent from wool scouring and sewage with high levels of COD, BOD and pesticides. The process consists of a combination of an evaporation and incineration plant and a biological effluent treatment plant. A high energy concentrate is produced by the evaporator and this is incinerated at 1200°C. All organic matter and pesticides are destroyed. The condensate from the evaporator is returned to the wool scouring process. The flue gas from the incinerator is fed to a boiler which serves a steam turbine and this generates sufficient electricity for the whole installation to be self-supporting in energy.

Treatment does not always take place within a plant that can be inspected. A number of learned papers have been written on the techniques that can be used for the *in situ* biological denitrification of nitrate-rich groundwaters[13].

TEMPERATURE

Variation in temperature of the feed liquor can cause convection currents in water and effluent settlement tanks, with consequent poor separation of solids. Although balancing tanks may smooth out temperature shocks, it is far better to avoid the loss of energy and to recover the heat within the factory process. High temperatures kill bacteria that can upset biological treatment. Low temperatures may affect biological treatment due to reduced biological activity. Different types of plant respond to cold weather in different ways — for example, an activated sludge plant aerated by surface aerators can be several degrees cooler than a similar plant aerated by sub-surface diffused air.

MONITORING, CONTROL AND MANPOWER

Choosing the right person for any job is important and the manning of water and effluent plants should be no exception. Besides the fact that the plant is fundamental to the operation of a site, day-to-day running of the process can be a fascinating and rewarding task.

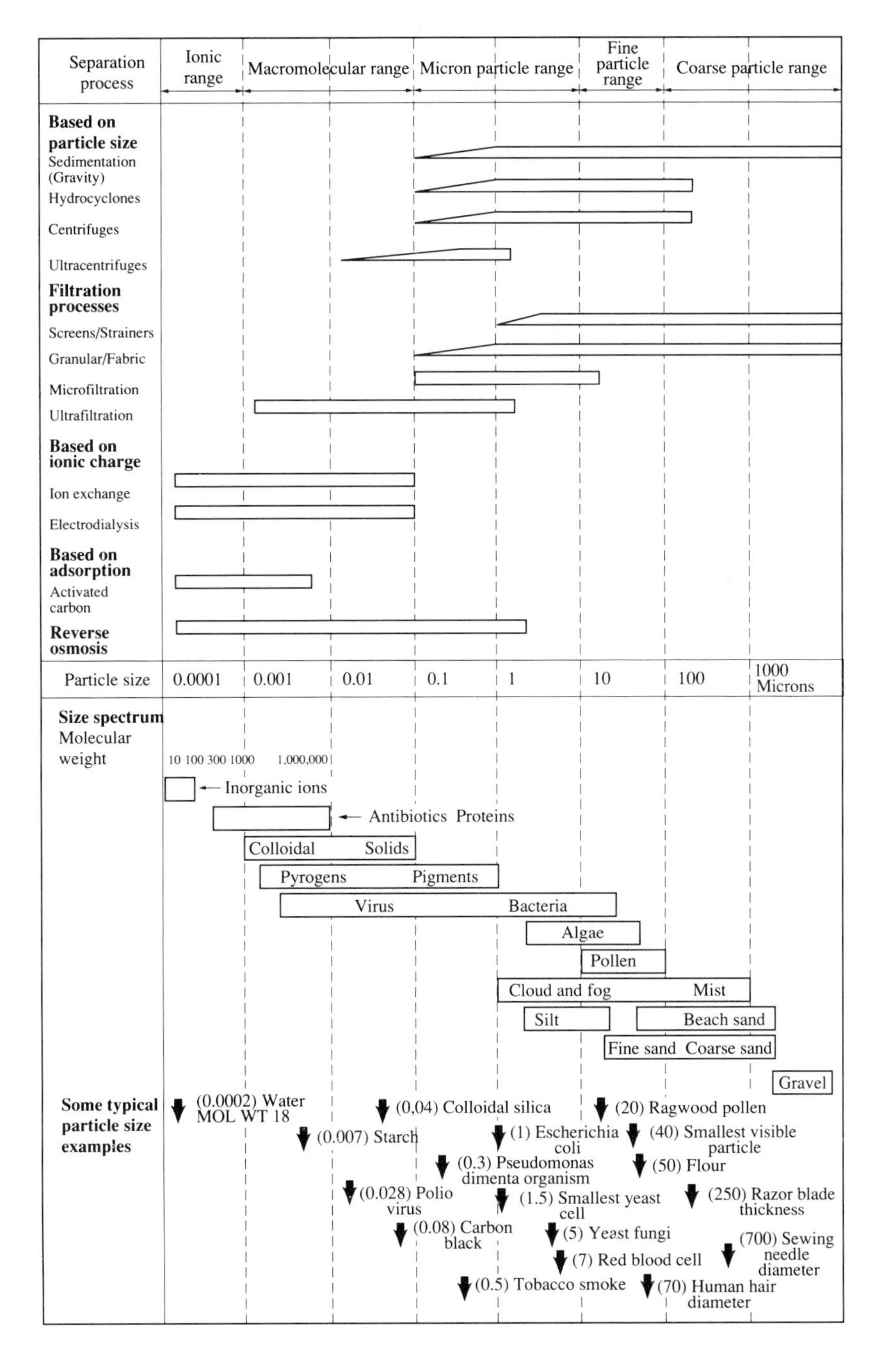

Figure 6.3 Separation processes against particle size. © British Water.

Having selected someone, will they have the correct training[14,15]? Has the plant supplier provided a comprehensive and intelligible operation manual for the plant? Can the plant supplier train the operator? If not, there are others who will[16–19]. Plant suppliers are also increasingly willing to provide regular maintenance and plant operating services, the latter often chargeable on the volume treated.

AUTOMATIC PLANT OPERATION

Many plants are installed to run automatically. Water utilities are steadily demanning small and medium treatment works and relying on instrumentation[20,21], control and automation (ICA) techniques and on telemetry (radio waves used to control remote plant). If there is a possibility of automating plant, it is advisable to speak to the designer or supplier of the original plant.

The means of arranging unattended operation can be simple. Most people have seen the pipes that form the rotary sewage distributor arms that slowly rotate over effluent treatment filter beds, spreading the effluent over the bed from small nozzles in the arms. Simple devices are available to enable these filters to be left unattended for long periods. One comprises a series of plungers that automatically clean the jets by moving in and out of the jet holes as they rotate. Another device is a sensor that detects the movement of the filter arms. The third involves the fitting of wind sails attached to masts on the filter arms to assist rotation during periods of low flow or adverse weather conditions.

Although remote control and monitoring is a practical proposition, it is advisable to keep things as simple as possible. On effluent treatment plants, sensors will be installed in tough conditions and much thought needs to be given to ensure that the sensors work well and give meaningful measurements. Thus, the positioning of the sensor and the way in which the liquid is presented to the sensor are of the utmost importance. The need for regular re-calibration and maintenance should not be overlooked. Solar or wind power can be used to operate monitoring equipment on remote sites.

AIR

Air is used for instrumentation (moisture should be removed from the air), for the flotation of suspended solids (inevitably there are many plant designs, and efficiencies vary), for the backwashing of filters and for the support of aerobic bacteria in the activated sludge treatment of effluents. In sludge treatment, air provides a readily available supply of oxygen. Maintaining the correct dissolved oxygen (DO) concentrations in an activated sludge plant is important. Excessive DO concentrations give low operation efficiencies, and effluent quality can be affected by DO concentrations which are too low. Control systems are available to maintain different optimum aeration intensities at various points in the plant.

OXYGEN

Oxygen is used in a pure form in effluent treatment, both as the basis for the treatment and also as a means of economical peak-lopping on other conventional plants. Oxygen is also used in emergencies — for instance, in accidental discharge situations in watercourses when valuable fish stocks are threatened.

ANAEROBIC TREATMENT

The anaerobic treatment of effluent demands that air be excluded, in order to allow the growth of methane-producing bacteria. The cost of control, the optimum use of the methane gas and the quality of the final effluent need to be considered (see under 'By-Products', page 112).

ENERGY CONSERVATION

Energy-saving techniques are now well documented and the approach is very similar to that used to highlight water and effluent savings. The best time to consider energy efficiency is when a plant is being designed. On existing water or effluent plant, an energy audit and the metering and graphing of energy use are good first measures. Abnormal usage highlights problems in the process, or with the item of plant itself. Knowing the proportion of energy used by each section of the process enables effort to be concentrated on the equipment with the greatest daily energy use. A small percentage energy saving on equipment with a large energy use may well save far more money than a large percentage reduction on equipment with a small need for energy.

Good regular maintenance of a plant can substantially reduce energy consumption. As an example, control of aeration intensities has an immediate link to energy savings, especially as energy for aeration represents a high proportion of the total energy costs on activated sludge works. Wessex Water is carrying out a trial on wind-powered aerators, at a small works treating sewage from about 250 people.

PLANT SIZE AND OPERATION

The sizing of storage or balancing tanks is closely related to on-site water or effluent treatment. Large storage is a form of insurance for the site, but there may be a limit on available site space. It is often better to run treatment plant for effluent continuously, even though most of the effluent is produced in an eight-to-ten hour working period. Taking two hours to treat the amount of effluent created in one hour not only makes a significant reduction in peak electrical demand but also a saving in capital cost. The balancing and mixing of crude trade effluent prior to treatment is likely to be beneficial for the treatment process too, as short shock loadings or swings in pH are dampened down during balancing. Balancing has helped Southern Water to reduce peak aeration demand at one works by up to a quarter, as well as improving the final effluent quality. A major electronics manufacturing company arranged for its effluent treatment plant to be built over the balance tank. Not only did this save site space but, more importantly, it ensured that if any item of plant ruptured or overflowed, the discharge would be contained in the balance tank.

The treatment of water and effluent inevitably involves the flow of liquids though pipes and vessels. Water is a heavy and expensive substance to move around but a proliferation of pumps and complicated pipework is not always the most sensible solution. Simple plant is often preferable and if gravity can be used to advantage, this is better still. Mains water enters a site at a pressure and it is reasonable to capture this pressure through high level storage. Sloping sites may be a developer's nightmare, but they can be a process engineer's dream.

Having said that, to move liquids to higher levels generally requires the use of pumps and pipework. Pump efficiencies vary enormously. An airlift pump may be only 10–25% efficient, whereas a multistage borehole pump can be over 80% efficient. The lower the efficiency, the more energy required for a given duty. There may be no alternative for particular airlift or other pump applications. But for the majority of purposes, it is worth checking if the pump is the most efficient for the task, or if variable-speed control would help. The higher cost often associated with more efficient pumps can usually be repaid by energy cost savings.

Some pumps have a tendency to lose their suction, resulting in the need to re-prime, with the associated lost time and production. Short vertical shaft pumps are available that have their impellers placed below the liquid level. When they start up they are automatically primed by the surrounding liquid; when they shut down, provided there is no non-return valve, the liquid can drain back through the pump into the wet well, thus avoiding the freezing of pipelines in winter and the cost of lagging.

When liquids flow though pipelines and fittings, there is head-loss due to friction. The greater the friction, through undersized pipework and fittings, the greater the waste of energy. It is worthwhile checking whether extra quantities are now being forced though old pipework or whether the inside diameter has been restricted by scale.

CHEMICALS

These are used in water treatment to encourage fine suspended matter to settle out and to disinfect[22] the treated water. Chemicals are used on some trade effluents to act as nutrients to aid the bacteria. Acids or alkalis are used to neutralize both water and effluent streams. Most bacteria used in effluent treatment do not like high or low pH levels. Extremes of pH will also contribute to the corrosion[23] of unsuitable materials of construction, for instance ferrous metals (mild steel, etc) at low pH, and aluminium at high pH. Above pH8 the effectiveness of chlorination in killing bacteria declines rapidly. As the pH rises above 8, there is an increasing tendency to encourage the precipitation of hardness salts.

An interesting and safer way of neutralizing alkaline effluents on sites with boilers could be the use of the boiler flue gas which contains the neutralizing agent carbon dioxide. Cost reductions of 60% or more are claimed, compared with the cost of hydrochloric acid.

Attempts have been made through a waste materials exchange to find a use for discarded chemicals. In theory this should reduce costs for the producer and for the user of the waste. Unfortunately, the potential purchaser of reusable waste needs a regular supply at a consistent quality and this is where the difficulties lie. However, the Industrial Research and Technology Unit, Lisburn, Northern Ireland, set up a Waste Exchange Bureau in 1993 with the intention of identifying alternatives to disposal for industrial wastes generated in Northern Ireland. The underlying motive is to promote improved waste management practices. Enquiries have been received from elsewhere in Europe.

Due to inevitable changes over time, both in the liquid to be treated and with the development of more sophisticated chemicals, it is recommended that a periodic check is made on the appropriateness of the quantity and quality of chemicals in use. Obviously this is not likely to be as important for chemicals with a long-established history of use, such as chlorine. However, the handling of chlorine[24,25] and chlorinated water and the required contact time[26] are important (see Chapter 5).

Severn Trent Water has installed an automatic coagulant control system at a water treatment works. The equipment has the dual effect of reducing the coagulant consumption and of increasing run times on the downstream filters.

A money-saving tripartite project has been initiated by ICI Watercare Australia, the Sydney Water Board and BHP in Sydney — Australia's largest steel manufacturers. The project involves converting BHP's tin mill from sulphuric to hydrochloric acid pickling. The spent acid is removed from BHP's plant by ICI Watercare and recycled to manufacture a flocculating agent to be used by the Sydney Water Board for chemically-assisted sedimentation of sewage and for sewage odour control.

The economics are always changing in relation to technology and consumables. Currently, the cost of membrane processes is reducing and the cost of chemicals and their disposal is increasing. The choice of regeneration chemicals for an ion exchange process can have a significant effect on the cost of the treated water — sulphuric acid is cheaper than hydrochloric acid. More expensive and stronger chemicals could become attractive when the capital cost of a process plant is written down over an extended period.

BY-PRODUCTS

By-products from a treatment process can sometimes be turned to advantage, as is the case with sludge from water and effluent treatment. In some industries the by-product can be valuable, with the recovery of precious or other metals from inorganic wastes. Sludge can be digested under anaerobic conditions to produce methane gas fuel and this process produces a more acceptable sludge for spreading on land[27,28]. Sludge can also be used as an ingredient for compost.

The Waste Management Consultancy of ADAS, Leeds, estimates that recycling of suitable wastes could save some of the £600 million that farmers spend on fertilizers each year[29].

Suitable high-strength organic effluents can be segregated and treated using anaerobic treatment methods[30]. Now that retention times needed in a digester — and consequently the size and capital cost — have been reduced, the anaerobic treatment of industrial organic wastes is becoming more attractive. The economics are improved if warm waste streams, such as cooling water, are available to help heat the digester. This frees all the methane gas produced for use, for instance, in boilers or as a fuel for a gas engine which can generate electricity.

Methane gas does not necessarily have to come from the site. Gas is being captured and piped away from large municipal waste tips and sold to adjacent factories. Before privatization, the Southern Water Authority came to an arrangement with a computer factory to supply gas from sewage digesters, instead of mains gas, to provide factory heating. The cost of the work has been shared and it should be recovered in less than two years.

Factories releasing animal or fish protein in the effluent may be suitable candidates for a treatment process incorporating the recovery of this protein. The protein is precipitated, using a compound made from a by-product of wood (lignosulphonate).

A chemical company developed a plant based on membranes, for its own use, which can deal with solids up to 50% in water-based effluents from surface coatings such as paints, polymers, emulsions, adhesives, sealants and inks. The technique is also applicable to strong effluents containing pharmaceuticals, fine chemicals, paper, drinks, textiles and food. Nearly 100% solids recovery is said to be achievable.

STANDARDS AND REGULATIONS

If a company operating a water treatment plant does not meet the in-house, UK or European standards (see Chapter 2), the consequences affect not only its product but also the people involved in the manufacture of that product.

Where effluent is treated and discharged to a sewer, or direct to a watercourse, then the regulatory body responsible will make sure that the discharge is kept up to standard. Consent conditions for discharges to sewer exist to protect the structure of the sewer, operators working in the sewer and the municipal treatment works itself. Similarly, standards for effluent discharged to a watercourse exist to protect the animals living in and on the water and the other users of that water.

Fish are used as an indicator of good and bad water. Trout do not live in a dirty river. Keeping fish in a treated effluent discharge pond, for instance, shows that it is considered suitably clean.

Regulations based on good sense, which are enforced with fairness, should be good for the environment and for the business enterprises to which they are applied.

SUMMARY AND CHECK-LIST

- Do not treat unless essential.
- Treat the minimum — recycle.
- Treat well.
- Monitor in and out.
- Select key characteristics to monitor:

— flows;
— quality;
— chemicals;
— energy;
— labour;
— maintenance.

- Up-rate, refurbish, automate and de-bottleneck old plant.
- Monitor new technology available.
- Operate and maintain to high standards.
- Consider energy savings.

- Optimize chemical performance.
- Instrument and automate where cost effective.
- Recover valuable waste products.
- Review statutory and advisory standards and regulations.
- Consider independent maintenance checks by your supplier.
- Manage and monitor the facility.
- Seek advice from the experts.

SOURCES OF INFORMATION

INFORMATION

1. Solt, G.S. and Shirley, C.B., 1991, *An Engineer's Guide to Water Treatment* (Avebury Technical).
2. Department of the Environment, Welsh Office and Scottish Office, 1993, *Manual on Treatment of Private Water Supplies* (HMSO). Produced to assist local authorities in discharging their responsibilities for private water supplies.
3. Hall, T. and Hyde, R.A., 1992, *Water Treatment Processes and Practices* (WRc).
4. *An Introduction to Sewage Treatment*, 1986 (Chartered Institution of Water and Environmental Management).
5. *Septic Tanks and Small Sewage Treatment Works. A Guide to Current Practice and Common Problems, CIRIA Technical Note 146*, 1993 (Construction Industry Research and Information Association).
6. House of Lords, 1993, *Industry and the Environment, Paper Number 73* (HMSO).
7. Screenings and grit in sewage: removal, treatment and disposal, *Technical Note 119*, 1984 (Construction Industry Research and Information Association). Also *Technical Note 122*, 1985.
8. *An Approach to the Testing of Process Plant for the Water Industry,* 1995 (WRc).
9. Department of Health, 1994, *The Microbiology of Water 1994. Part I. Drinking Water. Report on Public Health and Medical Subjects No 71. Methods for the Examination of Waters and Associated Materials* (HMSO).
10. Biodegradable plastic using activated sludge, *New Technology Japan, June 1992* (Japan External Trade Organization, Machinery and Technology Dept., 2–5, Toranomon 2-chome, Minato-ku, Tokyo 105, Japan).
11. Cremer and Warner, 1993, Thoughts on food effluent, *Environment Today,* Summer, 21–28.
12. *Standard for the Specification, Approval and Testing of Granular Filtering Materials — Appendices and Figures Cover Conversion Tables; Grading Charts and Apparatus, BEWA:P.18.93* (British Water).
13. Hiscock, K., 1990, Underground Treatment of Nitrate, *Water and Waste Treatment.*
14. *Enclosed Wastewater Treatment Plants — Health and Safety Considerations,* 1993 (Foundation for Water Research).
15. Health and Safety Executive, 1977, *Entry into Confined Spaces, GS 5,* (HSE Books).

16. *Aqueous Effluents — An Environmental Protection Training Package, E01*, 1992 (IChemE).
17. Specialist consultants — Association of Consulting Engineers, Alliance House, 12 Caxton Street, London SW1H 0QL, tel: 0171 222 6557, fax: 0171 222 0750 — British Water, see page 149 for details.
18. Water Training International, Tadley Court, Tadley Common Road, Tadley, Nr Basingstoke, Hants RG26 6TB.
19. The School of Water Sciences, Cranfield University, Cranfield, Beds MK43 0AL.
20. Russell, S., 1994, *WRc Instrument Handbooks — guides to measurement in water applications* (WRc).
21. The GAMBICA Association Ltd, Westminster Tower, 3 Albert Embankment, London SE1 7SW, tel: 0171 793 3050, fax: 0171 793 7635. The association for the instrumentation, control and automation industry in the UK.
22. World Health Organization, 1989, *Disinfection of Rural and Small-Community Water Supplies — A Manual for Design and Operation* (WRc Publications on behalf of WHO).
23. National Corrosion Service, National Physical Laboratory, Teddington, TW11 0LW.
24. Health and Safety Executive, 1992, *Management of Health and Safety at Work. Management of Health and Safety at Work Regulations 1992: Approved Code of Practice, L21* (HSE Books).
25. Health and Safety Executive, 1992, *Workplace Health, Safety and Welfare: Workplace (Health , Safety and Welfare) Regulations 1992. Approved Code of Practice, L24* (HSE Books).
26. *Chlorination of Drinking Water — A Short Guide to Process Design*, 1990, (British Water).
27. Ministry of Agriculture Fisheries and Food, 1989, *Code of Good Agricultural Practice for the Protection of the Soil (MAFF Publications).*
28. Department of Environment, 1989, *Code of Practice for Agricultural Use of Sewage Sludge* (HMSO).
29. Rudd, C., 1993, Don't waste waste — recycle it, *Environment Today*, Winter, 10–11.
30. *Biotechnology — Support and Regulations in the UK — A Plain Man's Guide* (Laboratory of the Government Chemist).

FURTHER READING

BS6068: Water Quality, Part 6 Sampling, Section 6.10: 1993 Guidance on sampling waste waters (British Standards Institution). Contains details on the sampling of domestic and industrial waste water.

BS6297: 1983 British Standard Code of Practice for Design and Installation of Small Sewage Treatment Works and Cesspools (British Standards Institution).

Civil Engineering Specification for the Water Industry, 4th edition, 1994 (WRc Publications).

Handbooks of UK Wastewater Practice. Glossary, second edition, 1993 (Chartered Institution of Water and Environmental Management).

The Process System Principle in the Water Industry, 1984 (WRc Publications).

Standard Method for Testing the Performance of Salt Regenerated Ion Exchange Water Softeners for Direct Connection to the Mains Water Supply — BEWA:P.19.93, 1993 (British Water).

Standard Method for Testing the Performance of Salt Regenerated Nitrate Removal Units for Direct Connection to the Mains Water Supply — BEWA:P.07.90, 1990 (British Water).

Standard Method for Testing the Performance of Activated Carbon-based Filter Units for Direct Connection to the Household Mains Supply — BEWA:P.09.93, 1993 (British Water).

Suppliers' technical literature and published papers.

Water Distribution, 1990 (Chartered Institution of Water and Environmental Management).

Water Research Centre technical reports on many water supply and sewage topics — for example, *TR 184 Polyelectrolyte Users' Manual* (WRc, Marketing Services).

7. CONTROLLING ON-SITE WASTAGE

INTERNAL MOTIVATION

'On-site' implies taking action, as opposed to discussing problems in the comfort of a remote office. It should involve all staff and operators on site. It is alternatively referred to as 'in-house' or 'in-factory'. Wastage control may embrace 'good housekeeping', 'effluent reduction', 'water management', 'yield improvement' or 'total process efficiency'.

Control is not always easy to achieve. It is, however, the key, for it is only through constant control over wastage that water and effluent charges will be permanently reduced to a minimum level.

THE PRINCIPAL BARRIERS TO BE FACED

There are two main hurdles to overcome. Firstly, in order to achieve optimum wastage control it may well be necessary to change the natural and unknowing actions of staff and operators. In most cases wastage occurs because people are not carrying out their duties efficiently or do not have the right equipment to do the job. Secondly, if it is desired to control something in a physical or engineering sense, it follows that it will be necessary to measure and fully understand the object of this control — 'if you can't measure it, you can't manage it'.

Some industries[1] have spent many years and much effort in creating control techniques that are now built into the daily factory routine. Knowledge and commitment enable them to know what water, effluent and product wastages exist and to keep them to a minimum. Energy savings will automatically emerge.

Product wastage has been mentioned. Society requires industries to produce a vast array of products, many of which involve the use of water in the manufacturing process. Consequently, it is only possible here to give general indicators which, it is hoped, should be applicable to many industries.

One estimate[2] of the potential savings in the chemical and refining industries is as follows:

- reductions in uncontrolled use — for example, poor housekeeping: 20–30%;
- improvements in control and management of existing water systems: 20–30%;
- reuse of water without treatment at other points in the process: 10–20%;
- treatment and recycle of water for further use in the process: 10–20%;
- improvements in process design so that water is not required: 10–20%.

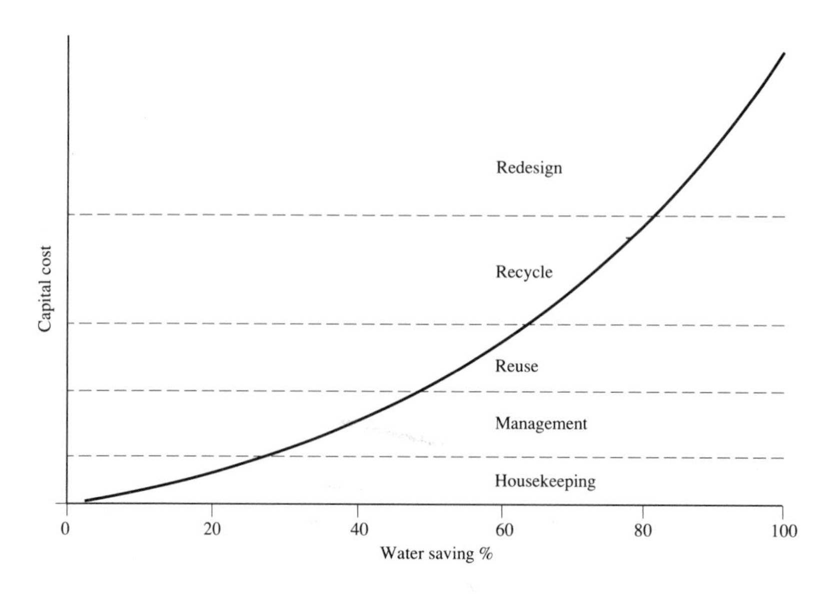

Figure 7.1 Capital expenditure relationship to water savings. (Source: IChemE.)

The list progresses from the simplest and cheapest to the most difficult and expensive. This relationship between capital expenditure and potential water savings is shown in Figure 7.1.

When raw materials and products have a moderate or greater value, it is by no means uncommon to find that, having set out to save on water and effluent charges, the greatest saving actually occurs in the value of the retained product. For example, work done in The Netherlands in the 1980s on effluents from over a hundred sites in the dairy industry allowed investigators to estimate that the value of the product saved would be about three times the value of the saving in the cost of effluent disposal. Projected savings at one UK dairy a few years ago revealed that for every £1 saved from reducing water losses, effluent savings could be £1.44, energy £1.44, but the value of the product saved could be £2.77!

Similarly, measures to reduce energy consumption often reduce water and effluent volumes. An example from the brewing industry is of wort boiled at 100°C and then cooled to about 10°C before fermentation begins. The cooling of the wort with water of suitable quality can produce liquor at 85°C which can be used as process water for the next mash.

A sequence of events which would lead to permanent on-site wastage control activity could be as outlined next.

STAFF MOTIVATION

It is of the utmost importance for as many people as possible to 'get the message'. As with many management matters, the interest and leadership has to come from the top, but the sooner things become a team effort, the better. Environment teams can be formed involving employees from across the company. The implications of excessive water use and product waste should be explained, perhaps through a company environment newsletter, in relation to the profitability of the company and the environmental impact on the community. Each person has to set a good example and whatever happens people should not be reprimanded. In other words, 'thank you for reporting the spillage', not 'what on earth were you doing to allow the spillage to take place?'! Prizes could be given to employees who come up with the best 'green' ideas.

THE SITE SURVEY

Motivation should lead to a desire to know if the site activities could be improved so that less product, water and effluent are lost down the drain.

A site survey is the best means of achieving this. Techniques can be learned, or someone in the industry may already be employing the techniques, or have a survey team which can be employed or give advice. Guinness Brewing Worldwide has an in-house audit team of three to five people, depending on site complexity[3].

If the site is large, consider starting with one department. What needs to be established is how much water comes on to the site, what is it used for and where does it go? To determine this it will be necessary to:

- trace all the water distribution pipework and produce a line diagram showing pipe sizes, storage tanks, plant served and actual, or maker's recommended, flow rates;
- draw up a water balance table showing the daily totals for each supply on the left of the table and where all the water goes on the right of the table. Do not overlook internal sources of supply, such as condensate which emerges when a product is boiled (evaporated) and the vapours condensed. Take account also of 'losses' such as water incorporated in a product or discharged to atmosphere from a cooling tower.

In the manufacture of wet-spun fibres, cellulose 'dopes' are injected through spinnerettes into precipitating 'spin-baths'. Over 30% of the process energy is used in the recovery of spin-bath liquor by multiple effect evaporation, in itself an efficient process. Hot condensate from the evaporators is often acid-contaminated and, at Courtaulds' plants, was previously rejected to drain. These liquors are now sent to the first, acid stages of the fibre washing process thereby reducing demand for both water and heat, and reducing effluent charges. At the time the improvement was made, savings were over £100,000 a year.

Assuming that the site uses water in the production area as well as for domestic purposes, then the fate of the water and product lost down the drain needs to be established. For example, are by-products discharged to effluent? Is surface water measured as effluent (see Chapter 3)? The Brewers Society advocates the setting up of centres of water consumption accountability to coincide with budgetary control centres.

To establish the discharge situation requires a number of steps to be taken. Firstly, it will be necessary to obtain a copy of the drainage plan for the site and to ensure that it is correct. Are streams of foul, surface water and trade effluent going down the appropriate drains?

Next, can the effluent be analysed in order to give results that will approximate to the amount of product lost down the drain? For organic products it is likely that the COD test can be used. Direct reading of pH, conductivity or turbidity may be possible. For survey purposes, suspended or dissolved solids or those able to settle are other useful tests. Ideally, the number and range of tests should be kept to the minimum necessary in order to assess what is going down the drain. For non-organic products, such as steel, tests could include not only analysis for iron, but tin, chromium, zinc, etc. For organic effluents, a modified 'product' test may be possible such as lactose, sucrose or protein in effluent. A pollution monitor has been developed which provides results on samples in 30 seconds, based on chemical luminescence. It is likely to be of assistance in tracing the source of pollution rapidly. When the source is traced and sampled, more conventional and accurate tests can be applied.

Establish which inspection chambers could be used for sampling and if there is a means of measuring the volume of effluent. Devices are available for measuring flow in existing drains and a number of different effluent samplers are on the market. For small or awkwardly placed discharges, samples can be taken using a long handled ladle, bucket and stop-watch.

The survey proper should establish the discharge pattern and characteristics over 24 hours and seven days per week. The solid foundation for the survey (and life after the survey) is the measurement of the water flow to the site or department. The degree of sophistication required to establish flows and pollution loads from items of plant and departments will vary from site to site. A bucket and stopwatch may suffice at one site, but full flow monitoring may be required at another.

The production and service activities which are sandwiched between the incoming water distribution pipework and the site drains need to be observed, again over 24 hours and seven days per week.

Discuss this survey activity fully and well in advance with the production plant operators and other site staff, to ensure as far as possible that the factory continues to operate in a normal way. Operators understand their plant and, if given the chance, can put forward valuable suggestions for better wastage control. Observe each piece of plant which uses water and handles product and assess water usage and product waste. There are two aims which are *central* to controlling on-site wastage. They are to establish:

- the **actual** water usage and product wastage;
- a reasonable minimum **target** level for water use and product waste.

There may be difficulties in isolating the discharges from items of plant so that they can be sampled and the flows assessed. Some minor pipework alterations may be required to facilitate the survey work.

Those doing the survey must ensure that they cover the inaccessible parts of the site. This includes climbing ladders to observe high level storage tanks or crawling through service pipe passages. Safety precautions must not be overlooked. In some locations, such as underground chambers, methane gas can be a hazard[4].

An inspection when the plant is not operating is usually most rewarding. As the site should be quiet, listening as well as observing could reveal the existence of water leaks — over 50 were detected in one night at one food industry factory site. Inspection chamber covers should be lifted at strategic points in order to observe what is being discharged and to check if there is infiltration of groundwater.

Many underground leaks occur without giving a visual indication on the surface. *The Plant Engineer*[5] reported that a UK Health Authority was set to save over £120,000 per year following a professional leak detection survey. Precise flow logging between 2 a.m. and 4 a.m., when actual water usage was practically zero, revealed an excessive flow. A number of leaks were then located in a subsequent leak detection and repair programme which gave a payback of less than a month.

Raychem can provide a longline system for laying in the false floors of computer rooms and service corridors to warn of leaks from pipes serving central heating and chilled water systems. The installation consists of a water-sensing polymeric cable connected to an electronic alarm module. The alarm sounds when the cable senses water and the distance of the leak from the module is shown on the display.

A number of UK consultants and contractors provide wastage control survey techniques on behalf of clients in many industries. A two-day survey at a bottled fruit drink manufacturer revealed that effluent flows could be cut by a third, saving £75,000 a year, by good housekeeping and by simple modifications to the manufacturing process. Another, but longer survey, compared operations at two poultry packing sites. One site was found to be operating well. Savings highlighted at that site were less than £15,000 a year. Savings at the other site were ten times greater. About 25% of the saving at the second site was achievable through the replacement of spot trade effluent sampling by 24 hour composite sampling in order to provide a fairer picture of the discharge quality (see the end of Chapter 6 and 'Trade Effluent', Chapter 3, page 53).

THE SURVEY REPORT

The survey report should be made available and discussed with the site management as soon as possible after the survey. The report should include the following, or similar, items:

An introduction

This incorporates the aim of the survey.

A general description of the survey and the results

This should include a general statement of what the survey found about the site water supply and drainage, and an explanation of how sampling and analysis were carried out. An explanation should be given of what the survey found in each department, including statements about average daily production; crude effluent loadings; an estimate of by how much the volumetric and effluent pollution loads could be reduced; ratios of product throughput to water or effluent flows; an assessment of non-product loads; a total or percentage of the product lost to drain per day, and — most importantly — the monetary value of the water, effluent and product savings which may be revealed, as well as energy.

Graphs should be used to show the pattern of daily and day-to-day water, effluent and product throughputs as well as effluent strengths and other parameters which may be relevant to the site, such as pH, conductivity, temperature, etc. Up-to-date water distribution and drainage diagrams for the site will also be of value.

It may also be possible to record savings which were identified by the survey and where immediate action was taken by the site staff to reduce the losses. Praise should be given to operators and staff in areas where good control is found. Lessons can be learned from good practices and ideas.

In order to give the maximum impact, water and effluent costs could be expressed as a percentage of the added value on the product. The leather industry does this. For instance, if the basic cost of a hide is 70 pence per unit area and it sells for £1.00, then the company has 30 pence for processing and

TABLE 7.1
Example of departmental summary

Department	Assessed average weekly totals		Achievable weekly totals	
	Effluent / m^3	COD / kg	Effluent / m^3	COD / kg
Intake	55.60	373	35.51	356
Product preparation	811.05	1104	126.38	690
Pressing	262.41	698	90.57	644
Cookhouse	321.87	2799	288.87	2009
Packing	101.62	321	52.62	271
Prepack	26.13	95	26.13	95
Small goods	957.47	2649	382.67	1522
Canning	100.66	385	61.12	364
Services	1270.89	1691	557.21	1564
Effluent plant	1181.86	53	63.22	13
Total	5089.56	10,168	1684.30	7528

Note: The table compares volumetric and COD loadings found during the survey with those considered possible if all recommendations are implemented.

profit. If water costs 0.9 pence per unit area, this is then presented as 3% of the margin between the cost and selling price.

Recommendations
These may be numerous, and because of this, priorities could be allocated to guide management on where initial effort should be concentrated if the recommendations are to be implemented. The recommendations can be set out under 'general', 'services' and 'departmental' headings. Weekly, or preferably daily, effluent loadings and volumes should be included and figures given for achievable targets (see Table 7.1). Typical recommendations are illustrated in Table 7.2 on pages 126 and 127.

Priorities (1 to 3, etc) can be decided upon by assessing the value of savings and the ease, or cost, of achieving them, and the contribution the savings make to the water-related efficiency of the site (see also Figure 7.1 on page 118). For those who are keen on mathematics, a water-pinch analysis can be used[2]. The analysis provides a graphical representation of how savings can benefit the site as a whole, or if particular savings are the best options in terms of cost and investment. The graphs plot the degree (concentration) of water contamination against the mass of water transferred through the process.

If applicable, a table should be incorporated setting out the water, water-related and product monetary values and the added costs for energy, softening and disinfection, etc, so that the real cost of discharging various liquids to sewer can be seen easily. A table or list can show potential sources and volumes of reclaimable water.

The survey results could point the way to the benefits of the separation, or concentration, of waste streams from a manufacturing process and to the designing out of water use and related effluent creation.

Finally, if it is relevant to the products manufactured on site, the report should give an example of a spillage report form, and any other relevant supporting information from the survey.

ACTION AND RESPONSIBILITIES

It must be decided whether on-site wastage control is of relevance to the site and, if so, everyone on site should be informed. Make staff aware of the existence of a wastage control policy. It should form part of the induction training for new employees at all levels[6].

Allied Colloids, in West Yorkshire, produced a 25-page in-house booklet on waste management, in order to spread its policy and action programme through the company. The management of the programme was explained, as well as how the workforce was to be involved. The company set out a five-step approach to getting started, under the following headings:

- management commitment;
- identify problem areas and opportunities;
- quantify the target;
- take action;
- maintain momentum.

The booklet then gave ten examples of waste minimization in practice. One such example relates to the manufacture of low molecular weight polymers (which contain solvent) for uses such as paint dispersants and boiler feed additives. Each solvent loss process was investigated and, by introducing minor process changes, the solvent content in the waste water passing to biological treatment was reduced and the solvent content of the product was reduced too.

An extra condenser was installed, reducing the loss to air and recovering solvent for reuse. The overall savings have been in excess of £40,000 per year. In 1990, the French chemicals group Rhône Poulenc set itself targets of 50% for the reduction of solid wastes and effluents by the year 1995, and 65% by the year 2000.

Appointing a wastage control officer

Appoint a wastage control officer, or someone with that task written into a wider job description, if one does not already exist. If the officer is good at the job but starved of help, funds or backing to enable savings to be made, create protection against accusations of failing to make or maintain savings. At some locations the appointment may need to be seen as temporary because others on site could feel that wastage control is not their responsibility. Ideally, all site personnel should be motivated so that they consider themselves to be 'wastage control officers' in their own work area and on the site as a whole. The role of 'the management' becomes all important.

Establishing a reporting system

Act to establish a means of taking daily measurements of water and effluent, together with the necessary sampling and analytical tests. Suitable daily report forms should be on the site manager's desk first thing each morning, showing the previous day's achievements against the target. The forms should include daily water usage, the ratio of water to product (and other relevant comparative bases), the quantity of effluent discharged, the effluent load (kg COD, for example, obtained by multiplying the effluent strength, in milligrams per litre, by the flow, in litres, over a given time period) and the percentage of product lost to effluent. Investigate adverse results.

Weekly and monthly performance should be reviewed and publicized against targets. Graphs and monetary values for savings are essential.

For instance, if the strength of crude effluent from a brewery is an average 1539 milligrams per litre COD and 13 cubic metres flows over a period of time, this would be equivalent to a load of 20 kilograms COD, or the loss of one barrel of beer (36 imperial gallons), current value about £20 within the brewery before excise duty is added.

A Bedfordshire brewery measures production efficiency by ratios covering water to product, brew liquor to product, steam to product, effluent to product effluent and effluent to water. It is important to use ratios to compare performance trends on one site, or in one department. Comparison between sites can be meaningful and is always of interest, but can be unfair and misleading if important site-specific circumstances are not taken into account.

Taking selective action

Action needs to be taken on high, then lower, priority items from the survey. If this throws an unfair load onto the site maintenance engineering staff, the company should seriously consider employing off-site engineering firms, or staff, to carry out agreed modifications.

TABLE 7.2
Typical recommendations that could emerge from a survey

- Consideration should be given to a staff member being given responsibility for on-site wastage control, perhaps with added responsibility for conservation of resources in general. The job description of all those on site should include a statement of responsibility for conservation of resources.
- Consideration should be given to the installation of further meters, at points listed, in order to monitor areas of plant with high water usage.
- Wherever possible, discharges to drain should be made visible so that losses can be detected.
- Samples of all ingredients and chemicals used on site (which could be discharged to drain) were analysed for COD and for their contribution to the effluent COD loading (see tabulation).
- Washings which can reach surface water drains must be directed to effluent drains.

Water saving 4 m^3 per week

- When self-cleaning screens are introduced, the need for screen washing should be removed. Fat recovery at source (as shown elsewhere in the survey report) should ensure that these screens operate efficiently. (This is the highest single water 'loss' located during the survey.)

Water saving 890 m^3 per week
COD saving 40 kg per week

- The recovery of fat for separate disposal from the condensate (direct steam injection) off the cookers should be investigated. This could be achieved by draining the base of the cookers and collecting the run-off for recovery.

COD saving 600 kg per week

- Floors in the dip tank area should be swept to remove gross meat and fat before washing down. A skip (colour coded) should be provided for this waste product and removed for separate disposal once per day. Caustic cleaning solutions are dumped after each clean. They should be collected for reuse after de-sludging and bringing back to strength by automatic addition of concentrated chemical. Dumping should occur when contamination of the solution reaches an unacceptable level. Product left in circuit A2 should be reclaimed to tank 7 before in-place cleaning starts.

Priority 1
Cost saving £63,000 per year

- Initial caustic flush should be reduced from 15 to 5 s, as should the second rinse water flush.

Total savings approximately 1080 litres per day
Total cost savings £3750 per year

- Faulty, blocked or oversized sprayballs should be repaired and/or reported in order to avoid excessive spillages.
- Unnecessary detergent loss from the central cleaning unit should be avoided by altering the top-level probe which controls detergent return to the tank.

Water saving 0.18 m^3 per day
COD saving 0.09 kg per day

- Start-up and shutdown of product filling machine should be into cartons (not for sale) the contents of which are then reclaimed.

Approximate COD saving 6.44 kg per day

- Water valve to the mixing machine should be repaired.

Water saving 1.08 m^3 per day
Cost saving £130 per year

- The pressure relief valve on the hot water hose calorifier should be repaired.

Water saving 14.40 m^3 per day
Cost saving £1670 per year

- The borehole-failure audible alarm should be repositioned where it can easily be heard. The extra cost for using mains rather than borehole water is £302 per day.

Priority 1

- The vehicle wash is fed by town mains water and this should be replaced by suitable reclaimed process water, halving the cost of the water used and saving detergent.

Priority 3

- The boiler feed-pump gland cooling water should be reclaimed or recycled.

Priority 1
Water saving 95 m^3 per day
Cost saving £11,840 per year

Mangement procedures should include the setting of daily effluent target loads and water consumption volumes, related to product throughput, and the routine publication of monetary savings achieved or not achieved.

Give consideration, in the light of cost savings achieved, to making money available to replace old and inefficient plant with new plant which will lose less product and use less water. Those who propose to replace hand-operated or pre-computer-controlled plant should check the performance of the new plant in relation to water use and product loss. When purchasing new process plant, specify acceptable levels of water and energy use and product loss. If this cannot be done, then ask those quoting for the plant to provide the information and appropriate guarantees.

Maintaining the action programme

Changes to a production plant mean the re-surveying of the changed operation and the revising of target loads and volumes.

Site re-surveys and the adjustment of targets can be carried out at reasonable intervals — perhaps three to five years for the former and when the moment seems right for the latter. However, this is second-best to an ongoing computer-based monitoring and targeting system[7]. The system should include closed loop feedback and provide a methodical way of recording any changes made to production throughput, plant and services and their effects on waste minimization.

The energy manager at Bass Brewers Ltd, Cardiff, has developed a system of linear regression in order to raise energy efficiency continuously through setting realistic targets. Production plans, seasonal changes and historical data are used to set targets 18 months in advance.

Obviously some simple psychology needs to be employed when setting targets! Hard-to-achieve targets may discourage people — it is far better to set targets that are reasonably easy to achieve and to adjust them periodically.

All this may seem to be over-elaborate and difficult to introduce. On-site wastage control needs determination and a conviction that the effort is worthwhile. Provided that such a regime will improve profitability, there should be little argument against introducing it on site.

EXTERNAL MOTIVATION

THE QUANTUM LEAP

Using the guidelines set out so far in this chapter, and information elsewhere in this book, a managing director or manager should have little difficulty in introducing an on-site wastage control system provided that the site staff are suitably motivated. However, motivation in relation to wastage control may be extremely difficult to maintain. Trying to enthuse management and staff can be difficult. This is especially so at production sites where inconsistent orders have to be fulfilled by deadlines and where all the rules are broken to ensure that the deadlines are met.

As reported in United Nations Environment Programme *Industry and Environment*[8], in 1988 the Netherlands Organization of Technology Assessment launched a large-scale investigation into the prevention of waste and emissions in ten Dutch industrial companies. The project was given the name PRISMA (Project Industrial Successes with Pollution Prevention) and was partially funded by government. The aims of PRISMA were to:

- show Dutch industry that beneficial waste prevention was possible in the short term;
- test the usefulness of a systematic approach;
- establish the obstacles and formulate the conditions under which prevention can be made to work;
- formulate recommendations for an effective prevention policy.

The work to be carried out was based on the US Environmental Protection Agency's *Waste Minimization Opportunity Assessment Manual*[9] and other manuals. A total of 35 areas of priority were investigated in the ten companies. Within these areas, 164 waste 'prevention options' were established. Good housekeeping measures effected 25–30% reductions in the use of chemicals. The use of alternative raw materials gave rise to a 100% reduction in the emission of substances like cyanide in the zinc plating process at electroplating plants.

In the ten PRISMA companies, waste stream flows in production processes were reduced by 30%. Despite this, the PRISMA team came across four types of financial obstacles:

- vested interests;
- low charges for the disposal of waste streams;
- funding;
- incomplete calculation and allocation of environmental costs.

Project experience shows that intensive guidance and company-oriented consultancy can eliminate a substantial number of these obstacles.

Among the recommendations from the PRISMA team are:

- government should give clear priority to the appointment of prevention teams to stimulate, supervise and advise companies;
- government should give greater priority to prevention-orientated demonstration projects within companies;
- better co-ordination at regional level between various organizations involved in the transfer of knowledge;

- there should be a direct link between regulations and waste and emission prevention;
- the formulation and implementation of waste prevention plans should be a condition for granting a licence;
- government should monitor the existence and progress of waste prevention programmes.

In the UK, key national and regional bodies have become involved, thus enabling a quantum leap to take place in spreading the gospel of on-site liquid wastage control through demonstration projects. One such was the Aire and Calder Project whose sponsors were:

- the BOC Foundation for the Environment[10], which was launched in 1990 with the principal objective of supporting practical research and demonstration projects which aim to show how pollution could be reduced in the UK;
- HMIP, which sees the objects of such projects fitting well with its role in relation to the Environmental Protection Act 1990 and the need to prevent, minimize and render harmless those substances covered by the Act;
- NRA, which is required to conserve and manage water quality and resources. The NRA believes that waste minimization is a very important development to improve the water environment in a sustainable and cost-effective way. So much so, that a significant section of its Corporate Strategy document published in 1994[11] is devoted to 'Collaboration and partnership'. The NRA wishes to work with partners to pre-empt regulation and encourage voluntary action. It stresses that a massive investment in sophisticated technology is not necessary for success;
- Yorkshire Water decided to co-sponsor the study because environmental improvement is central to its mission and because it is aware of the damaging long-term effects of toxic levels of discharge from industry and thus the benefits of removing as much of this as possible at source.

The project was initiated by the Centre for Exploitation of Science and Technology (CEST), as a result of its 1992 report *Water: Resource and Opportunity*.

The project was based on a river catchment, which was seen as conferring a number of advantages:

- all participating companies have a common interest in the health of the rivers (there are 11 participants, but 98 firms were approached — perhaps this ratio is a measure of the untapped potential and the mammoth task ahead);
- some participants abstract water from the rivers;
- the focus on the small geographical area provides a link between the participants, the community and the local media;
- a variety of industries could be involved;

• news about the project could be disseminated locally — for instance, through chambers of commerce, and nationally through trade associations with which the participants were linked.

Reports are available[12], which show that in the first 18 months of the project the 11 participating companies made savings of over £2 million per year. Potential savings are greater still. Just over 10% of the measures to reduce waste were cost neutral. A further 60% had a payback of less than one year.

The contract to manage the project was given to the March Consulting Group[7]. Because of the financial support from the sponsors, the participating companies only had to pay 50% of the consultancy costs.

At a project-related seminar in July 1994, organized by the NRA and the Confederation of British Industry (CBI), the following points emerged:

• total commitment of senior management (Board level) is essential;

• there has to be an effective 'project champion' within each participating company in order to maintain momentum;

• focussing on a geographic rather than an industry sector means that there is less competition between companies, with the result that they are more willing to share information and experiences. The atmosphere is more supportive, with the slower-moving companies being stimulated by the faster-moving ones. Furthermore, a great sense of community emerges amongst the participating companies;

• the project showed that companies which follow a structured approach gain the most (that is, the adoption of formal targeting and monitoring);

• 540 ways to reduce wastage emerged from the 11 sites (being in a club broadens your knowledge and options);

• the big savings come by reducing inputs;

• a number of similar projects have been or are being organized in locations such as the Mersey Basin (Project Catalyst); Leicestershire; Oxfordshire (Oxfordshire Business Environmental Group); West Midlands (Waste Minimization West Midlands); Severn Estuary; Eastern Counties (River Cam catchment); Thames Valley; Teesside; Humberside; River Dee in Wales; Rivers Sheaf, Rother and Don in South Yorkshire;

• because of the overwhelming evidence of financial gain, especially for large companies, it is unlikely that future projects will be subsidized;

• particular attention is to be paid to the needs of small-to-medium-sized enterprises (SMEs) and how to involve them in such projects.

Project Catalyst[2,13], listed above, involved 14 companies over 16 months and revealed 400 ways of cutting waste. Savings by early 1994 were £2.3 million, with £3.7million more expected in the following year. One food canning company found that steam traps serving cookers and sterilizers were being blocked by food from defective cans and grease from conveyors. This discovery was after the steam traps had been by-passed to enable condensate to be removed. This modification had inevitably meant a continuous discharge of steam, with attendant energy loss and the heating of the surrounding work area. Project Catalyst led to the design of baffles, to contain the steam losses, at a cost of £25,000. But it yielded energy savings of £50,000 per year and a six-month pay back.

A paper in the *Journal of the American Water Works Association*[14] in October 1991 gave details of how industries in California — encouraged by municipalities, water suppliers and other agencies — had made savings. One case study which covered 15 sites showed typical reductions in water use of between 20 and 40%.

In 1993, the regulator for the privatized UK electricity industry announced a proposal for electricity distributors to spend £1 per customer on energy efficiency. Perhaps the water industry will follow suit, in relation to water use and the creation of effluent.

YOUR BUSINESS AND THE ENVIRONMENT

Business and the Environment[15] has published a workbook entitled *Your Business and the Environment*. It is intended for companies who wish to look wider than the use of water, loss of product and the creation of effluent. It encourages the reader to look at the issues, develop a framework environmental policy and carry out a total assessment of the current environmental position and performance of a company or site.

QUALITY ASSURANCE, ENVIRONMENTAL AUDITING AND EMAS

Possible vehicles to carry formal procedures for on-site wastage control have existed in the form of British Standard (BS) 5750 — Quality systems (now changed to BS EN ISO9000) and BS7750 — Specification for environmental management systems.

For those who are unfamiliar with the above standards, in essence BS EN ISO9000 enables quality systems to be developed and implemented for internal quality management purposes, in relation to the design and supply of a product or service.

BS7750 was developed from BS5750. It covers the requirements for the development, implementation and maintenance of management systems aimed at ensuring compliance with stated environmental policy and objectives. The quality systems approach of BS5750 was used. BS7750 can be applied to any organization or type of industry, including services and manufacturing. There are procedures to cover those who are already certified under BS5750 and who wish to expand the systems to include environmental management under BS7750.

BS5750/ BS EN ISO9000 and 7750 could also be the steps along the way to total quality management to BS7850: 1992. Part 1 of the standard — Guide to management principles — is aimed at senior management. Part 2 — Guide to quality improvement methods — deals with the implementation of a continuous quality improvement process, as applied to every aspect of the organization. The waste minimization loop used by participants in the Aire and Calder Project was essentially the same as the BS7750 loop.

The Eco-Management and Audit Scheme (EMAS) was published by the EC in July 1993. This voluntary scheme, which is aimed at industry, is effective from April 1995. There are suggestions that when the regulation is renewed in the year 2000 it may become mandatory in some sectors of industry.

The April 1994 issue of *Environmental Manager*[16] published a review of the results of a survey of 17 companies by PA Consulting Group. PA tried an EC pilot exercise to test the draft Eco-Management and Audit Regulation. EMAS site accreditation requires participating companies to decide on an environmental policy and strategy, set objectives, set up an environmental management system, initiate an audit and review programme to assess environmental performance, show commitment to external validation (an important feature, but an on-cost) and make information on environmental performance available to the public by way of a statement. Included in the statement must be a summary of environmental policy, the management system, emissions, waste generation, consumption of raw materials, energy and water, and a summary of improvement targets.

The Regulation, like BS7750, is not intended to be an absolute measure of management performance in relation to environmental protection. It does provide a standard which shows that effective systems are in place for managing the environment.

The PA Consulting Group pilot study found that the introduction of formal environmental management systems increased management's confidence in the workforce and the activities carried out. Interestingly, few of the participating companies found actual cost savings in terms of reduced energy consumption and a reduction in waste since most of them had already optimized these aspects. This would seem to reinforce the need for the surveying, targeting and monitoring techniques outlined earlier in this chapter.

HELP FROM ELSEWHERE

As could be expected, the Department of Trade and Industry supports the concept and practice of waste control[17]. Those who wish to collaborate with other companies can form a Waste Minimization Club. Part of the costs of setting up and running the Club may be eligible for support. Clubs can be based on a particular sector of industry or on a particular geographic region. The DTI Environment Unit can provide further information.

The IChemE's *Waste Minimization: A Practical Guide*[9] has been written to provide overviews of the practical techniques which can be implemented to minimize waste (solid and hazardous — although much of the contents is applicable to water and product savings) and also the methods which can be followed to ensure that waste minimization programmes and projects are successfully implemented. Minimization techniques are as illustrated in Figure 7.2. The Institution has also produced a slide training package on aqueous effluent control[18].

In June 1994 the Environmental Technology Best Practice Programme was launched (as the Minister mentions in his Foreword to this book on page v). It is a joint initiative by the DTI and the DoE. It aims to promote better environmental performance and to increase the competitiveness of UK industry and commerce. The Programme is managed on a day-to-day basis by AEA Technology through ETSU and the National Environmental Technology Centre.

The main themes of the Programme are waste minimization and cost-effective cleaner technology. The Programme collects, analyses and publicizes information on the most effective measures available. By emphasizing the reduction and elimination of waste and pollution at source, the Programme will

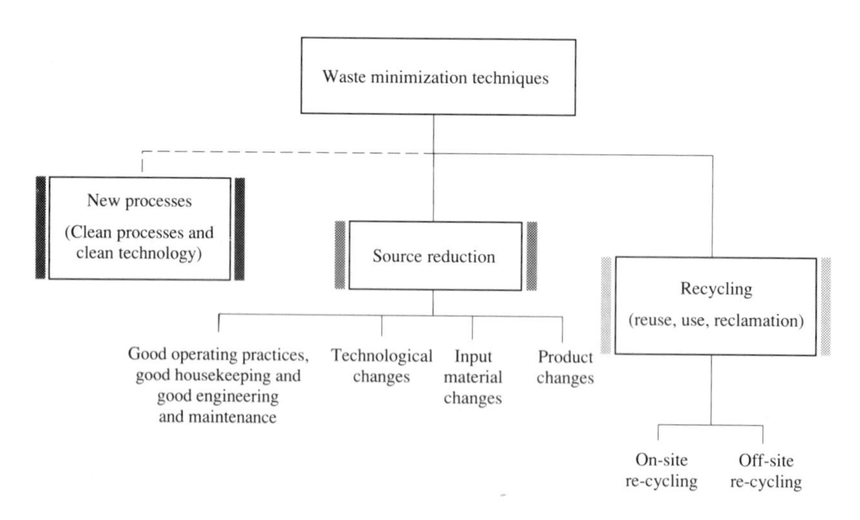

Figure 7.2 Techniques for waste minimization. (Source: IChemE.)

encourage and help companies to improve both their environmental and economic performance.

In addition, special attention is being focused on particular areas where there are seen to be substantial environmental and commercial benefits. The areas designated so far are foundries; volatile organic compounds (VOCs); metal finishing/surface engineering; textiles; glass; printing; paper and board manufacturing. Other special areas will be added later.

The Programme provides all sectors of industry and commerce in the UK with information and advice on environmental technologies and techniques. This is achieved through five closely-integrated elements. These are:

- an environmental helpline[19] offering up to two hours' free advice;
- environmental performance guides — giving benchmark information;
- good practice guides and case studies —to promote proven technologies and techniques, where a participating host company for a good practice case study can receive an access payment of up to £10,000;
- new practice — to encourage the spread of new environmental technologies and techniques, with access payments of up to £50,000 for the participating host company;
- future practice — where research and development can be supported financially for up to 49% of eligible costs.

One way to tackle a problem which cannot be solved by current technology is to collaborate with a university. The Engineering and Physical Sciences Research Council (EPSRC)[20] has a clean technology programme, which aims to support research into ways of forestalling pollution, taking into consideration issues of sustainability, energy efficiency, waste minimization and recycling. Research on the cleaning up of water is supported by the built environment programme, which relates to towns, roads, etc. The EPSRC gives funds to universities for precompetitive, non-commercial research, which can be in collaboration with companies.

SOURCES OF INFORMATION

REFERENCES IN CHAPTER 7

1. *Guide for Dairy Managers on Wastage Prevention in Dairy Plants, IDF Document 124*, 1980 (International Dairy Federation, Belgium).
2. Newton, D. and Solt, G., 1994, *Water Use and Reuse* (IChemE). Contains chapters entitled Is zero aqueous discharge a practical option?, Defining a strategy for fresh water and wastewater minimization using water-pinch analysis, Project Catalyst — a waste minimization demonstration project.
3. Wheeler, R.E., 1992, Environmental auditing of brewing activities, *Managing*

Resources for Profit Conference, York, 5 November 1992 (Brewers' Society/Energy Efficiency Office).

4. *Factories Act 1961* (HMSO). Section 8 sets out precautions which have to be observed where work has to be done inside any chamber, tank, pit, pipe, flue or similar confined space, in which dangerous fumes are liable to be present to such an extent as to involve risk of persons being overcome, or where the proportion of oxygen in the air is liable to have been substantially reduced.
5. Water leak detection, 1993, *The Plant Engineer*, 37 (4): 5.
6. *Pollution Prevention Pays* (NRA). Free pack containing video, book and poster with simple guidelines to help industry prevent pollution.
7. *The Aire and Calder Experience — A Short Management Guide*. Free from March Consulting Group, Telegraphic House, Waterfront 2000, Salford Quays, Manchester M5 2XW.
8. de Hoo, S. and Dieleman, H., 1992, UNEP Industry and Environment, 15 (1–2): 52–62.
9. Crittenden, B. and Kolaczkowski, S., 1995, *Waste Minimization: A Practical Guide* (IChemE). Based on the US Environmental Protection Agency guide. Includes case studies in the field.
10. The BOC Foundation for the Environment, 70 Shenfield Road, Shenfield, Brentwood, Essex CM15 8EW.
11. *NRA Corporate Strategy*, 1994 (Corporate Planning, NRA).
12. *Waste Minimization: a route to profit and cleaner production. An interim report on The Aire and Calder Project*, 1994 (CEST, 5 Berners Road, Islington, London N1 0PW). Also available: case studies for the ten companies participating in the Project and a video 'Waste Minimization' describing the achievements of the Aire and Calder Project and Project Catalyst.
13. WS Atkins–North West, March Consulting Group and Aspects International, 1994, *Project Catalyst. Report to the Demos Project Event, Manchester Airport, 27 June.*
14. Manzione, M., Jordan, B. and Maddaus, W.O., 1991, California industries cut water use, *J Amer Water Works Assn*, October, 55–61.
15. *Your Business and the Environment — A DIY Review for Companies,* 2nd Edition, 1994 (Business in the Environment).
16. Eco-audit regulation, 1994, *Environmental Manager*, 1 (8): 5–8.
17. *Cutting Your Losses 2 — A Further Guide to Waste Minimization for Business,* 1992 (DTI, Environment Unit). Contains information on support schemes and many encouraging examples of the way in which named companies have made significant monetary savings. The first edition was published in 1989.
18. *Slide Training Package in Aqueous Effluents*, 1992 (IChemE). Contains all the technical, legal and visual information needed to train staff in aqueous effluent control and treatment techniques.
19. Environmental Technology Best Practice Programme Environmental Helpline, 0800 585794.

20. Engineering and Physical Sciences Research Council, Polaris House, North Star Avenue, Swindon SN2 1ET.

FURTHER READING AND SOURCES OF ADVICE

Environment Costs. The Effects on Competitiveness of the Environment, Health and Safety, 1994 (Confederation of British Industry).

Institute for Environmental Assessment (IEA), Gregory Croft House, Fen Road, East Kirkby PE23 4DB, tel: 01790 763613, fax: 01790 763630. Exists to help improve standards in environmental assessment and consultancy. Keeps a list of environmental consultants.

8. COPING WITH DROUGHT AND INTERRUPTION

There is no telling when the next drought will hit the temperate British Isles, or when water or effluent services will be affected by a breakdown, or perhaps industrial action. Following either a drought or an interruption to supplies, a review of what has been learned from the experience is to be recommended.

DROUGHT

In this century severe droughts have occurred in England and Wales in 1921, 1933–34, 1959, 1975–76, 1984 and from 1988 to 1992[1]. Within drought affected areas, the period between February 1990 and July 1992 was the driest consecutive 29 month period in England and Wales since the 1850s. Each drought is usually different in duration and in the land areas affected. Obviously the effect is worse, as in 1976, when it is preceded by a dry summer, autumn and winter.

Since the concept of regional river basin management was introduced to England and Wales in 1974, the NRA and water undertakers are increasingly in a better shape to deal with dry weather conditions[2]. Prior to the recent long drought, most of the much-needed reservoirs and other resources had been constructed — very few more were expected to be needed this century — and long interconnecting water mains had been laid. The lessons learned from coping with droughts are taken on board by the water industry. The recent drought and talk of the 'greenhouse effect' have prompted the NRA to publish overviews on water resources[3,4]. Transfer schemes, using canals for instance, are to be investigated and costed. Understandably, drought was one of the items covered in a recent NRA strategy document[5].

If it is especially important for an organization to have warning of dry conditions, rainfall information may be recorded on site or obtained from the Meteorological Office in Bracknell[6] (see Figure 8.1). It might also be worthwhile to investigate the possibility of an advance warning from the local water undertaker or water resources regulator. Obviously water undertakers will mount their own publicity campaigns when water resources become dangerously low, but they are unlikely to signal warnings to the public before it is really necessary. Equally, they will not wish the warnings to be too late.

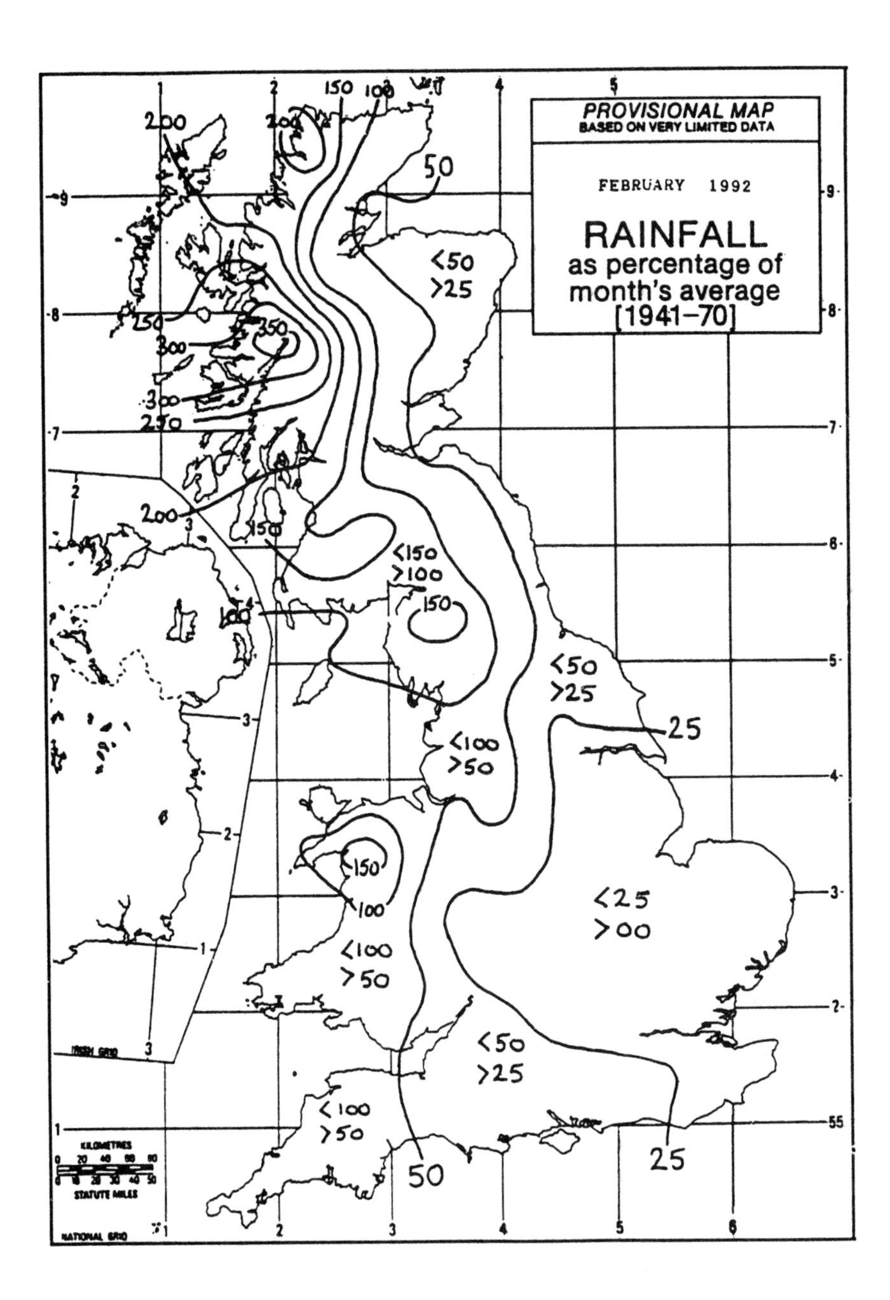

Figure 8.1 Rainfall as a percentage of monthly average. (Source: Meteorological Office.)

Monthly rainfall figures for a region, or from a number of gauging stations within a region, expressed as a percentage of the rainfall over previous years, provide — at a price — one simple indicator which can be used. It is important, however, to be aware that figures for a region can mask local differences. Alternatively, pointers and publicity sometimes appear in the local paper, or other media. Advance warning of the 1976 drought was given to a large group of companies by the author in early March 1976, based on the following 1975 rainfall information for England and Wales. The percentages relate to the worst and best regions in which the particular group operated:

- August 50–70% of 1916–50 average rainfall;
- September 100–120% of 1916–50 average rainfall;
- October 30–75% of 1916–50 average rainfall;
- November 60–75% of 1916–50 average rainfall;
- December 40–65% of 1916–50 average rainfall.

STATUTORY POWERS FOR WATER CONSERVATION

Powers to enable water undertakers to deal with drought situations are contained in Chapter III of Part II of the Water Resources Act 1991. It does not apply to Scotland, where the Water (Scotland) Act 1980 has to be used, nor to Northern Ireland, which relies on Article 36 of the Water and Sewerage Services (Northern Ireland) Order 1973.

Water undertakers, under section 76 of Part III of the Water Industry Act 1991, can prohibit the use of hosepipes for watering private gardens and washing private cars. This is normally the first step to be taken and is likely to be in place before an application is made for a drought order.

In England and Wales, the NRA or a water undertaker can apply for an Ordinary Drought Order. If the Secretary of State for the Environment is satisfied that an exceptional shortage of rain or a serious deficiency of supplies of water exists or is threatened, he may make an order containing provisions to meet the deficiency. Water undertakers can prohibit or limit the non-essential use of water and restrict discharges, including the discharge of trade effluent. The non-essential uses prescribed by the Department of the Environment include watering of gardens and lawns, filling of swimming pools and ponds, car washes, and the washing of road vehicles, cleaning the exterior of buildings (the manual cleaning of windows was exempt in the Drought Direction 1991), fountains and automatic flushing cisterns. As a result the NRA or others could, for example, be authorized to take water from a specified source, discharge water (subject to conditions) or prohibit taking water from a specified source if it seriously affects supplies available to the NRA or water undertaker. The Secretary of State can make the authorization for an initial period up to six months and can extend the period up to one year from the original commencement date. The powers conferred by an Ordinary Drought Order are discretionary. A water undertaker is not obliged to restrict the use of water for, say, washing road vehicles where the undertaker is satisfied that maximum recirculation of water is being achieved. The Department of the Environment has indicated that it would regard it as unreasonable for an undertaker to refuse to consider making exceptions of this kind.

If the situation is more serious, the NRA or a water undertaker may apply for an Emergency Drought Order (none made so far!). This may be granted if the Secretary of State is also satisfied that the water deficiency is such as to be likely to impair the economic or social well-being of persons in the affected area. The NRA may apply for the type of provision covered by an Ordinary Drought Order. In addition, a water undertaker may ask for provisions to prohibit or limit the use of water for such purposes as the water undertaker thinks fit and to supply water by standpipes or water tanks. The Secretary of State can make the authorization for a period up to three months, extendable up to five months. He also has the authority, which does not exist for Ordinary Drought Orders, to give directions on the use of Emergency Drought Order powers.

Both Ordinary and Emergency Drought Orders include general provisions which can include the NRA exercising powers to ensure as far as possible that supplies of water to a water undertaker are not seriously affected; a sewage undertaker may modify consents or agreements relative to the discharge of trade effluent to enable the sewage undertaker to comply with any conditions imposed on it by the order. The orders may make different provisions for different cases and different persons' circumstances and locations.

The powers may be applied to consumers generally, to a class of consumer or to a particular consumer. Those who contravene the Act can be prosecuted and those who have suffered damage can be compensated under certain circumstances. For instance, following an Ordinary Drought Order, compensation is payable for 'damage sustained' if the undertaker restricts legitimate use of a natural water source, or if it enters or occupies land and the owner or occupier is injuriously affected. When water shortages have created an emergency (covered by an Emergency Drought Order) compensation is payable for 'damage sustained' as a result of the entry on to land by the undertaker. It is not the intent of the Act, nor the policy of water undertakers, to pay compensation for a reduction in, or loss, of mains supply or a reduction in mains pressure. Where a metered supply exists, the agreement is worded accordingly.

Until the Drought Act 1976, commerce and industry had to take second place to householders but, since the Act, water undertakers can decide on priorities, taking all consumers into account. This must be within the scope given to them by the Drought Order.

During the 1984 drought, orders made under the Acts covered:

- reduction of compensation water from reservoirs to rivers;
- increased abstraction from rivers and boreholes by water undertakers;
- banning non-essential uses in critical areas;
- introduction of standpipes or rota cuts (not implemented due to the success of temporary drought works and a small amount of rain).

A temporary deterioration in river water quality is a usual consequence of drought in the UK. The reduced river flow means less dilution is available for municipal and industrial treated effluent discharges to the river. Also, when a drought breaks, river quality will often deteriorate further before recovering. Sub-standard water abstracted from the river, for treatment in a water treatment works, could affect the quality of the treated water.

ACTIONS TO MINIMIZE DIFFICULTIES

Possible actions have much in common with those described in Chapters 4 and 5. The saving techniques in those chapters, if not yet implemented, should be used where applicable. Because the homes of employees will be affected, it may be that consumption rises for domestic areas of the site. Any drought disruptions that affect the way the public lives may also affect the working of industry and commerce.

In the event of drought, it is a good idea to appoint a senior staff member, if such an appointment does not already exist, to be responsible for reducing water usage (see Chapter 7). An early task for the appointee should be to establish, if it is not already known, where the site water supply comes from and where the site effluent goes to. By establishing these facts and knowing the contact point within the local water undertaker or water resources regulator, it will be easier to assess the position as the drought progresses. All employees should be involved in the campaign to save water, in the factory and in the homes as well. Posters and stickers are usually obtainable from local water undertakers and can be effectively displayed. The water undertakers themselves will publicize the situation. South West Water used banner-towing aircraft and a balloon to put over the vital 'save water' message in 1989. In 1990, Mid Kent Water asked customers for water-saving ideas. The response from a five year old boy was quite simple — don't wash!

Meters should be read regularly, and the readings and production output plotted on a graph placed in a prominent position in the factory. When the factory is shut down and quiet, a survey can be arranged to spot and stop leaks. At least once per day water storage tanks and the distribution system should be inspected.

Where possible, supplies should be throttled back. Washing machines and dishwashers should only be used when they are full. If practicable, disposable cups, cutlery and plates can be used in canteens to reduce washing up, and cold or limited hot meals provided. Solids should be swept up from floors or cleaned out from process plant using little or no water. This was one of the most widely applied water saving methods in the 1976 drought.

Under drought conditions, a dirty vehicle will reflect a serious attitude to the situation. Vehicles should only be washed for purposes of health, hygiene or safety, and it is preferable to use a bucket rather than a hose (this could be covered by a Drought Order).

If practicable, a sealed plastic bag full of water could be placed in cisterns; alternatively, a clean brick sealed in a plastic bag can be used. Urinal flushing times should also be reduced. Automatic flushing could be banned by a Drought Order.

It may be possible to open up a disused well or borehole on the site or obtain water from a nearby watercourse. If this seems a possibility, the proposal must be discussed with the local water resources regulator (temporary licences may be needed in England and Wales) and precautions must be taken against hazards such as methane gas in underground chambers, rotten timber or corroded steelwork in wells, and chemical or microbiological contamination of the water source.

Agriculture could consider turning to trickle instead of spray irrigation. The system uses plastic hose lines, laid along crop rows, from which carefully controlled amounts of water are released to the root zones of individual plants.

In 1992, the Isles of Scilly Council commissioned a desalination plant which uses sea water as a source to provide drinking water, to augment the natural water supplies on the main island.

INTERRUPTION TO WATER SERVICES

Interruption to water supply or effluent discharge could occur within premises, or the source of the trouble could be external. Some of the causes are discussed here.

ELECTRICAL FAILURE

Within premises electrical failure should be minimized by good maintenance and suitable equipment replacement programmes. A few decades ago submersible pumps in boreholes were withdrawn for inspection every year or two. Due to the increase in maintenance costs, it is often more economic to allow that type of pump to run until it reaches the end of its useful life. If this is the company's policy, then the consequences of failure should be thought through, or minimized, by having a standby borehole, a spare pump suitably stored (open ends of pumps in store can become waste bins!) or a rapid-response maintenance contractor.

Power failure in the external grid system may well affect the whole process. The consequences will be known and may already have been experienced. Important sites can sometimes be provided with more than one electrical feeder (or source of mains water supply) and on-site generation can be installed to run the bare essential plant items in a process, in order to save product or raw materials or to stop the product setting solid. A small generator in a cheese factory paid for itself during a two-day power failure in Scotland.

FAILURE OF MAINS WATER SUPPLY

The mains supply can fail for many reasons. Water undertakers clean their mains from time to time. New connections or improvements have to be made to the distribution system. When this occurs, a warning should be given to customers (ask for the undertaker's Guaranteed Standards Scheme) — the duration of the cut-off is normally short. When a mains supply is re-charged after shutdown, the water is often discoloured and contains some suspended particles. If a process is sensitive to sub-standard water quality, then the water will have to run to waste until it clears. Someone in the factory should be made responsible for checking the water quality, if such quality is important. If the supply is routed through a large storage tank, the water may clear by the time it reaches the supply pipe from the tank to the factory. The suspended particles removed from the water will sink to the bottom of the storage tank and will thus hasten the necessity of cleaning out the tank.

In Leeds in December 1985, a 1066 mm (42 inch) diameter, 100-year-old main burst, resulting in the temporary loss of 40% of supply to the city. Some 140,000 people were without normal supplies for up to five days, during which time standpipes and water tankers provided emergency supplies. An emergency of this scale is fortunately very rare and many industrial water consumers may consider that it is virtually impossible to plan for normal production under such severe circumstances. Nevertheless, it is worthwhile considering such an event and drawing up plans in advance on how to cope with the situation. The amount of storage is important. In England and Wales the water company has to pay compensation under certain circumstances (see undertaker's Guaranteed Standards Scheme).

Extremely cold weather settled over the UK throughout February 1986. In early March there was a thaw and, as a result, the number of burst pipes in London rose to around 50 per day, which is five times the winter average.

Under the circumstances some consumers were affected by pressure drop or loss of supply until repairs were carried out.

INDUSTRIAL ACTION IN THE WATER INDUSTRY

Although widespread industrial action has been threatened on several occasions, the only time — in recent years — that the UK water industry has had to face an all-out strike by manual workers and some craftsmen which affected water services in England, Wales and Northern Ireland, was for 32 days starting 24 January 1983. Approaching 100,000 consumers (about 0.2% of the national total) were without a mains supply due to unrepaired bursts, etc, and about one in six of the population had to boil water before consumption, as a precaution, because of inadequate water treatment. Also, partly-treated effluent was discharged to many watercourses, but overall the effects were not as bad as had been feared. Some consumers were subject to rota cuts whilst others were affected by local pump failures. Fortunately, no major emergencies occurred which could not be coped with, but difficulties were experienced in backwashing filters at some water treatment works and in dealing with burst water mains. Since the strike, most water undertakers have increased their investment in remote control systems which, theoretically, would lessen still further the impact of any future industrial action.

EFFECTS OF SHORT-TERM DISRUPTION

Short-term water industry industrial action of, say, one or two days would have no effect on private water supplies. It would probably have no effect either on municipal and private effluent treatment plants (ETPs).

Isolated problems associated with mains water quality due to trouble with treatment, pumping plant or chlorination, are possible but unlikely. Consumers at greatest risk will be those taking direct off the mains and without storage.

Mains water pressure could be affected. Repairs to burst mains or to malfunctioning plant may not be carried out immediately.

ACTIONS TO MINIMIZE DIFFICULTIES

In order to minimize problems, it is important to keep up to date with developments. Maintain a list of names, locations and telephone numbers of local mains water distribution personnel. If in doubt, and especially if the water quality will affect the bacteriological or chemical quality of a product, more extensive measures could include:

- stepping up the frequency of monitoring chlorine in mains water;
- maintaining a visual check on quality (sample from a tap, direct off mains, into glass container);

- holding small quantities of mains water to cover essential needs for the following day. Do not hold water for more than 24 hours — find a subsequent use for this stored water. If appropriate, check on chlorine levels;
- checking if the quality of water being put into the water undertaker's distribution system has deteriorated — find out how many hours, or days, it takes for the water to reach the premises;
- economizing in the use of the mains water supply.

EFFECTS OF LONG-TERM DISRUPTION

Long-term disruption is not likely to affect private water supplies except possibly supplies of chlorine or water treatment chemicals. However, if river water is the source and is privately treated, the quality of the river could deteriorate, thus affecting the water treatment process. Similarly, it will have no effect on private ETPs unless chemicals are used and supplies are affected. Municipal plants, on the other hand, are likely to be progressively affected, resulting in untreated or partially treated effluent being discharged to watercourses.

The effect on mains water quality will depend on national or local policy and on the nature and duration of the industrial action. If a water undertaker decides that only water suitable for drinking will be put into the distribution system, then continuity of supplies is likely to suffer to the point that it would eventually lead to a drought-type situation, in which water was only available or allowed to be taken during specified hours of the day, or was distributed from tankers or standpipes. Although the mains water might be fit to drink, the chemical quality and appearance would probably deteriorate, which might make the water unsuitable for certain factory uses. Shutting off the supply may also create quality problems when the supply is restored. If the level of water in factory storage tanks is reduced abnormally, quality may be affected by disturbance of sediment. Inspect tanks and clean them regularly. Water undertakers have a list of priority consumers which will include hospitals and essential food manufacturers.

If a water undertaker decides that water unsuitable for drinking should be distributed, then the effect on individual activities within premises will have to be considered separately. If mains water comes from boreholes alone, and is unsuitable due to lack of chlorination, factories may be able to remedy the situation. If the quality is affected in other ways, seek further advice from the water supplier.

Mains water pressure may well be affected and bursts go unattended or the affected main may be isolated, together with those connected to it. The consumers at greatest risk are those taking water direct from the mains and without storage facilities. If effluent is discharged to the municipal sewer and has to be pumped to the treatment works and the pumps stop, effluent will back up through the drains. Under these circumstances little can be done about continuing effluent-creating processing or manufacture within premises so affected. Risks and complications must be borne in mind, such as the possible back-up of domestic effluent. A deterioration in water or effluent services to the extent that public health is put at risk would hopefully be avoided.

ACTIONS TO MINIMIZE DIFFICULTIES

The comments under 'Short-Term Disruption' (see page 145) also apply here. Action depends on local circumstances. Sites with private water supplies and effluent treatment plants are unlikely to be affected and thus may have a crucial role to play, especially if they are part of a group of companies. Give extra attention to water and effluent saving and to the quality of water which may affect the quality of the final product. In relation to the latter, the local Environmental Health Officer can advise and help. Many of the problems can be alleviated by actions taken within commerce and industry.

SOURCES OF INFORMATION

REFERENCES IN CHAPTER 8

1. *Hydrological Data UK — The 1988–92 Drought*, 1994 (Institute of Hydrology).
2. *Drought Management and its Impact on Public Water Systems: Report on a Colloquium Sponsored by the Water Science and Technology Board*, 1985 (National Academy Press).
3. NRA, 1994, *Water — Nature's Precious Resource* (HMSO).
4. Water Resources Development Strategy — A Discussion Document, 1992 (NRA).
5. *NRA Water Resources Strategy*, 1993 (NRA).
6. Meteorological Office, Room 710, London Road, Bracknell, Berkshire RG12 2SZ.

APPENDIX — USEFUL ADDRESSES

British Standards Institution (BSI)
Linford Wood
Milton Keynes MK14 6LE
General tel: 01908 220022
Ordering/price information tel: 01908 221166
Information Services tel: 01908 226888
General fax: 01908 320856
The national standards body for Britain. Helps British industry compete effectively in world markets. Many British Standards are listed in the 'Sources of Information' sections.

British Water
1 Queen Anne's Gate
London SW1H 9BT
Tel: 0171 957 4554
Fax: 0171 957 4565
A merger of the British Effluent and Water Association and the British Water Industries Group. Serves the water and waste water industry worldwide. Brings together operators, consultants, contractors, manufacturers and suppliers of equipment and services.

Chartered Institution of Water and Environmental Management (CIWEM)
15 John Street
London WC1N 2EB
Tel: 0171 831 3110
Fax: 0171 405 4967
Aims to advance the science and practice of water and environmental management for the public benefit. Promotes education, training and research in these areas.

Department of the Environment (DoE)
Romney House
43 Marsham Street
London SW1P 3PY
Tel: 0171 276 3000
Fax: 0171 276 0818
A UK Government department. The DoE Water Directorate is responsible for water policy and legislation, in England, including the system within which OFWAT, the NRA, the DWI and the water industry work.

Department of the Environment Northern Ireland (DoENI) (Water Services)
Northland House
3–5A Frederick Street
Belfast BT1 2NR
Tel: 01232 244711
Fax: 01232 330790
The department responsible for water in Northern Ireland. See page 22.

Department of Trade and Industry (DTI)
151 Buckingham Palace Road
London
SW1W 9SS
Tel: 0171 215 5000
Fax: 0171 215 2909
A UK Government department.

Drinking Water Inspectorate (DWI)
see **Department of the Environment**
Part of the UK Government's Department of the Environment. Responsible for the quality of drinking water. See page 21.

Foundation for Water Research
Allen House
The Listons
Liston Road
Marlow SL7 1FD
Tel: 01628 891589
Fax: 01628 472711
A private company limited by guarantee, committed to promoting research on water and related environmental issues of concern to its members.

Her Majesty's Inspectorate of Pollution (HMIP)
see Department of the Environment
Part of the UK Government's Department of the Environment. See page 21 and 43.

Industrial Water Society
35 Broomfield Avenue
Fazeley
Tamworth B78 3QB
Tel: 01827 289558
Fax: 01827 250408
Interested in all uses of water in industry and commerce. Members include manufacturers, suppliers and users.

International Water Supply Association
1 Queen Anne's Gate
London SW1H 9BT
Tel: 0171 957 4567
Fax: 0171 222 7243
Concerned with public water supply through pipes and the exchange of information worldwide.

National Rivers Authority (NRA)
Rivers House
Waterside
Aztec West
Almondsbury
Bristol BS12 4UD
Tel: 01454 624400
Fax: 01454 624409
An independent statutory body for England and Wales. See pages 16, 41, 57, 60 and 61.

Office of Water Services (OFWAT)
Centre City Tower
7 Hill Street
Birmingham B4 4UA
Tel: 0121 625 1300
Fax: 0121 625 1400
A central Government department protecting the interests of customers of the water and sewerage industry in England and Wales. See page 20 and 45.

Scottish Office Environment Department
Engineering, Water and Waste Directorate
27 Perth Street
Edinburgh
EH3 5RB
Tel: 0131 556 8400
Fax: 0131 244 2903
A central Government department within which the Directorate deals with water, sewerage, water pollution control and waste management and disposal services in Scotland. See page 23.

Water Companies Association
1 Queen Anne's Gate
London SW1H 9BT
Tel: 0171 222 0644
Fax: 0171 222 3366
The association for 19 of the water supply companies in England and Wales.

WRc plc
PO Box 85
Frankland Road
Blaygrove
Swindon SN5 8YR
Tel: 01793 511711
Fax: 01793 511712
A leading European research and consultancy organization, specializing in the areas of water, waste water and general environmental management.

WRc plc
Henley Road
Medmenham
Marlow SL7 2HD
Tel: 01491 571531
Fax: 01491 579094
Address of the WRc bookshop.

Water Services Association (WSA)
1 Queen Anne's Gate
London SW1H 9BT
Tel: 0171 957 4567
Fax: 0171 957 4666
The association for the ten water and sewerage companies in England and Wales.

Water undertakers
see under 'Water' in local telephone directory. Publications available cover current charges and charging schemes and Water Bye-laws.

WSA Publications
St Peter's House
Hartshead
Sheffield S1 1EU
Tel: 0114 273 7331
Fax: 0114 275 0998
The publishers of Water Services Association publications such as *Waterfacts*.

INDEX

A

abstraction iii, 25
  charges 55, 56
air 108
Aire and Calder Project 130
anaerobic treatment 109, 112
Appointment 20
automatic plant operation 108
average charges,
  measured trade effluent 2, 11
  measured water supply 1, 11

B

balancing tanks 109
BATNEEC (see best available techniques not entailing exessive cost)
best available techniques not entailing excessive cost (BATNEEC) 22
best practicable environmental option (BPEO) 22
biochemical oxygen demand (BOD) 55, 106
BOD (see biochemical oxygen demand)
boiler feedwater 77
bottle washer 87
BPEO (see best practicable environmental option)
burst rinsing 78
business discount tariffs 40

C

calcium carbonate solubility 81
capacity charges 42, 43
capital
  contribution 27
  cost 38
  expenditure 38, 118
Central Scotland Water Development Board 23
charges 3
  abstraction 55, 56, 58, 59
  capacity 42, 43
  for discharge to rivers 57
  for flood protection 50
  for land drainage 50
  for measured sewerage 50
  for measured water supply 49
  for principal services 45
  for rain and surface water 50
  for sea outfall 54
  for trade effluent 51, 52
    Mogden formula 52
  for unmeasured sewerage 48, 50
  for unmeasured water supply 46, 48
  incentive 41
  infrastructure 43
  initial costs 43
  outlook 2
  usage 42
Chemical Release Inventory 22
chemical oxygen demand (COD) 53, 55, 77, 106
chemicals 111
chlorine 72
  contact tank 73

CIP (see cleaning-in-place)
cleaner technology 82
cleaning 77
cleaning-in-place (CIP) 79
COD (see chemical oxygen demand)
codes of practice 29
'common carrier' concept 41
condensate 75
Consent to the Discharge of Trade Effluent 32
contamination 73
cooking the product, water for 86
cost-based tariffs 40
costs,
- initial 42
- operating 38
- of steam leaks 75, 77

court action 41
Cryptosporidia 102
Customer Service Committees, OFWAT 20, 45

D

Department of the Environment Northern Ireland (DoENI) 23
detergents 77
- and trade effluent discharges 88

discharge to rivers charges 57
DoENI (see Department of the Environment Northern Ireland)
domestic sewage (legislation) 31
drainage diagrams 122
Drinking Water Inspectorate (DWI) 21
drought 138
- Ordinary Drought Order 140
- Emergency Drought Order 141

DWI (see Drinking Water Inspectorate)

E

Eco-Management and Audit Scheme (EMAS) 133
effluent loadings 123
effluent treatment,
- in-house 99
- private services 28
- public services 26

electrical failure 143
EMAS (see Eco-Management and Audit Scheme)
Emergency Drought Order 141
energy conservation 109
England 16, 18, 37
environment agencies 22
environmental,
- auditing 132
- monitoring 61
- protection 61
  - US laws 8

European Community iii
European Environment Agency 22
evaporative cooling 93

F

factories, water use in 71
filtration, size of particles 107
fire-fighting 95
flocculation iii
flood protection charges 51
floor and yard washing 95
flow control valves 66
flow,
- quality 103
- quantity 103

G

gardens 95

H

hard water 80
heating 91
heavy metals 26
Her Majesty's Inspectorate of Pollution (HMIP) 21, 43
HMIP (see Her Majesty's Inspectorate of Pollution)

I

incentive charging 41
industrial action 145
infrastructure charges 43
in-house treatment of effluent 99
initial costs 43
inset appointments 41
instrumentation 108
integrated pollution control (IPC) 21, 43
interruption to water services 143
ion exchange iii
IPC (see integrated pollution control)

L

land drainage charges 50
leak detection 29, 121
Legionella 74, 93
legislation 29
leisure 95
long-term disruption 146

M

mains water iii
  supply failure 144
maintenance 63
measured sewerage charges 50
measured tariffs 47
measured water supply charges 49
metering 64
  coupling device 65
micro-organisms 104
milligram per litre (mg/l) iii
milk pollution 88, 89
misuse of water in the process industries 74
Mogden formula 52
monitoring 102, 131
motivation,
  external 128
  internal 117

N

National Rivers Authority (NRA) 16, 41, 57, 60, 61
  charges for discharges 60
  income 45
nitrate sensitive areas 25
nitrate vulnerable zones 24
Northern Ireland 23, 37
  Water Executive 23
NRA (see National Rivers Authority)

O

Office of Water Services (OFWAT) 20
  Customer Services Committees 20, 45
OFWAT (see Office of Water Services)
once-through cooling 92
operating costs 38
Ordinary Drought Order 140
oxygen 109

P

paper and board-making processes 96
  water recirculation 90
pH iii, 88
'polluter-pays' principle 7
pollution control 21
  integrated 21, 43

population growth 6
pressure reducing valves 66
pre-washing containers 86
principal services charges 44
PRISMA (see Project Industrial Successes with Pollution Prevention)
private effluent treatment 28
private water supplies 25, 31
product savings 118
product wastage 117
Project Catalyst 131
Project Industrial Successes with Pollution Prevention (PRISMA) 129
public water supplies 24, 29
pumps 74, 110

Q

quality assurance 132

R

rain and surface water charges 50
rainfall 140
rateable value 46
recycling treated effluent 95
recovery of heavy metals 26
registers 4, 22
regulations 29
reverse osmosis 24
rinsing of containers 86
river purification boards (Scotland) 23

S

Scotland 23, 37
Scottish Environmental Protection Agency 24
sea outfall charge 54
sea water 24
sensitive products 84
separation processes against particle size 107
services charged direct to customers 39
sewage iv
  odour control of 111
  treatment (see effluent treatment)
sewerage iv, 25
short-term disruption 145
showers 67
site surveys 119
sludge disposal 126
softened water 77, 80
Special Category Effluent 32
spray irrigation 58
spray taps 67
statutory responsibilities 15, 17
Statutory Water Quality Objectives 20
steam leaks 75
  cost of 76
stopvalve water metering coupling device 65
storage,
  of recovered water 72
  of water 71
  tank 73
surface water supplies 24
survey,
  departmental summary 123
  recommendations 123
  reports 122
sustainable development 5
swimming pools 95

T

targeting 131
target levels,
  product waste 121
  water use 121
tariffs,
  measured 47
  unmeasured 46

temperature 74, 106
toxicity-based consents 20
trade effluent iv, 32
  charges 51, 52
    average 2, 11
  pH 88
  sampling 55
  Special Category Effluent 32
  strength 55
  Trade Effluent Notice 32
transporting the product, water for 86
treated effluent discharges
  (legislation) 32
treatment plants 103, 108
  check-list 113

U

ultraviolet (UV) light 84
underground water supplies 24
unmeasured sewerage charges 48, 50
unmeasured tariffs 46
unmeasured water supply
  charges 46, 48
urinal flushing controls 67
usage charges 42

V

value added tax (VAT) 45

W

Wales 16, 18, 37
washing the product, water for 85
wastage control 118
  officers 125
waste,
  exchange 111
  management 6, 124
  minimization 124, 134
  Minimization Club 134
  plugs 68
  water treatment decision route 100
water,
  abstraction 25
    charges 55, 56
  audits 119
  Bye-laws 30
  closet cisterns 68
  conservation 140
  consumption patterns 28
  cycle 14
  disposal patterns 28
  for cooking the product 86
  for transporting the product 86
  for use in the product 85
  for washing the product 85
  hardness 80
  only companies iv, 16
    income 45
  pinch analysis 123
  Protection Zones 19
  recirculation units 90
  resources system 14
  saving devices 66
  savings 118
  service companies iv, 16
    income 45
  supplies 24
    average charges 1, 11
    public 24, 29
    private 25, 31
    sea water 24
    surface water 24
    underground 24
  supply company iv
  undertakers (definition) iv
  uses within factories 71
  utilities iv, 16

Z

zero emissions 84